www.EffortlessMath.com

... So Much More Online!

✓ FREE Math lessons

✓ More Math learning books!

✓ Mathematics Worksheets

✓ Online Math Tutors

Need a PDF version of this book?

Please visit www.EffortlessMath.com

ALEKS Math Prep 2020

A Comprehensive Review and Step-By-Step Guide to Preparing for the ALEKS Math Test

By

Reza Nazari & Ava Ross

All inquiries should be addressed to:

info@effortlessMath.com

www.EffortlessMath.com

ISBN-13: 978-1-64612-147-2

ISBN-10: 1-64612-147-3

Published by: Effortless Math Education

www.EffortlessMath.com

Description

ALEKS Math Prep 2020, which reflects the 2020 ALEKS test guidelines, provides students with the confidence and math skills they need to ace the ALEKS Math test. This comprehensive Prep book with hundreds of examples, over 2,500 sample questions, and two full length ALEKS Math tests is all you will ever need to fully prepare for the ALEKS Math. It will help you hone your math skills, overcome your exam anxiety, and boost your confidence -- and do your best to succeed on the ALEKS Math Test.

Whether you are intimidated by math, or even if you were the first to raise your hand in the Math classes, this book can help you incorporate the most effective method and the right strategies to prepare for the ALEKS Math test successfully. **ALEKS *Math Prep 2020*** is a breakthrough in Math learning — offering a winning formula and the most powerful methods for learning basic Math topics confidently.

The surest way to succeed on ALEKS Math Test is with intensive practice in every math topic tested--and that's what you will get in **ALEKS *Math Prep 2020*.** Each chapter of this focused format has a comprehensive review created by Test Prep experts that goes into detail to cover all of the content likely to appear on the ALEKS Math test. Not only does this all-inclusive workbook offer everything you will ever need to conquer ALEKS Math test, it also contains two full-length and realistic ALEKS Math tests that reflect the format and question types on the ALEKS to help you check your exam-readiness and identify where you need more practice.

Inside the pages of this comprehensive prep book, students can learn math topics in a structured manner with a complete study program to help them understand essential math skills. It also has many exciting features, including:

- Content 100% aligned with the 2020 ALEKS test
- Written by ALEKS Math tutors and test experts
- Complete coverage of all ALEKS Math concepts and topics which you will be tested
- Step-by-step guide for all ALEKS Math topics
- Over 2,500 additional ALEKS math practice questions in both multiple-choice and grid-in formats with answers grouped by topic, so you can focus on your weak areas
- Abundant Math skill building exercises to help test-takers approach different question types that might be unfamiliar to them
- 2 full-length practice tests (featuring new question types) with detailed answers

ALEKS Math Prep 2020 is the only book you'll ever need to master Basic Math topics! It can be used as a self–study course – you do not need to work with a Math tutor. (It can also be used with a Math tutor)

Ideal for self-study as well as for classroom usage.

About the Author

Reza Nazari is the author of more than 100 Math learning books including:
– **Math and Critical Thinking Challenges:** For the Middle and High School Student
– **GED Math in 30 Days**
– **ASVAB Math Workbook 2018 - 2019**
– **Effortless Math Education Workbooks**
– **and many more Mathematics books ...**

Reza is also an experienced Math instructor and a test–prep expert who has been tutoring students since 2008. Reza is the founder of Effortless Math Education, a tutoring company that has helped many students raise their standardized test scores—and attend the colleges of their dreams. Reza provides an individualized custom learning plan and the personalized attention that makes a difference in how students view math.

You can contact Reza via email at:
reza@EffortlessMath.com

Find Reza's professional profile at:
goo.gl/zoC9rJ

Contents

Operations with Polynomials 103

Answers – Chapter 12 104

Chapter 13: Geometry and Solid Figures 106

The Pythagorean Theorem 107

Triangles 108

Polygons 109

Circles 110

Trapezoids 111

Cubes 112

Rectangular Prisms 113

Cylinder 114

Answers – Chapter 13 115

Chapter 14: Statistics 117

Mean, Median, Mode, and Range of the Given Data 118

Histograms 119

Pie Graph 120

Probability Problems 121

Permutations and Combinations 122

Answers – Chapter 14 123

Chapter 15: Quadratic 124

Solving a Quadratic Equation 125

Graphing Quadratic Functions 126

Solving Quadratic Inequalities 127

Graphing Quadratic inequalities 128

Answers of Worksheets – Chapter 15 129

Chapter 16: Complex Numbers 131

Adding and Subtracting Complex Numbers 132

Multiplying and Dividing Complex Numbers 133

Rationalizing Imaginary Denominators 134

Answers of Worksheets – Chapter 16 135

Chapter 1: Fractions and Mixed Numbers

Math Topics that you'll learn in this Chapter:

- ✓ Simplifying Fractions
- ✓ Adding and Subtracting Fractions
- ✓ Multiplying and Dividing Fractions
- ✓ Adding Mixed Numbers
- ✓ Subtracting Mixed Numbers
- ✓ Multiplying Mixed Numbers
- ✓ Dividing Mixed Numbers

"A Man is like a fraction whose numerator is what he is and whose denominator is what he thinks of himself. The larger the denominator, the smaller the fraction." –Tolstoy

Simplifying Fractions

Step-by-step guide:

- ✓ Evenly divide both the top and bottom of the fraction by $2, 3, 5, 7, \ldots$ etc.

- ✓ Continue until you can't go any further.

Examples:

1) Simplify $\frac{18}{24}$.

To simplify $\frac{18}{24}$, find a number that both 18 and 24 are divisible by. Both are divisible by 6.

Then: $\frac{18}{24} = \frac{18 \div 6}{24 \div 6} = \frac{3}{4}$

2) Simplify $\frac{72}{90}$.

To simplify $\frac{72}{90}$, find a number that both 72 and 90 are divisible by. Both are divisible by 9 and 18. Then: $\frac{72}{90} = \frac{72 \div 9}{90 \div 9} = \frac{8}{10}$, 8 and 10 are divisible by 2, then: $\frac{8}{10} = \frac{4}{5}$

or $\frac{72}{90} = \frac{72 \div 18}{90 \div 18} = \frac{4}{5}$

✎ *Simplify each fraction.*

1) $\frac{8}{6} =$

2) $\frac{4}{16} =$

3) $\frac{13}{26} =$

4) $\frac{21}{28} =$

5) $\frac{30}{45} =$

6) $\frac{8}{48} =$

7) $\frac{15}{45} =$

8) $\frac{22}{26} =$

9) $\frac{28}{54} =$

10) $\frac{35}{75} =$

11) $\frac{49}{63} =$

12) $\frac{38}{50} =$

Adding and Subtracting Fractions

Step-by-step guide:

- ✓ For "like" fractions (fractions with the same denominator), add or subtract the numerators and write the answer over the common denominator.
- ✓ Find equivalent fractions with the same denominator before you can add or subtract fractions with different denominators.
- ✓ Adding and Subtracting with the same denominator:

$$\frac{a}{b} + \frac{c}{b} = \frac{a+c}{b} \ , \ \frac{a}{b} - \frac{c}{b} = \frac{a-c}{b}$$

- ✓ Adding and Subtracting fractions with different denominators:

$$\frac{a}{b} + \frac{c}{d} = \frac{ad+bc}{bd} \ , \ \frac{a}{b} - \frac{c}{d} = \frac{ad-cb}{bd}$$

Examples:

1) Subtract fractions. $\frac{2}{3} - \frac{1}{2} =$

For "like" fractions, subtract the numerators and write the answer over the common denominator. then: $\frac{4}{6} - \frac{3}{6} = \frac{4-3}{6} = \frac{1}{6}$

2) Subtract fractions. $\frac{3}{7} + \frac{2}{3} =$

For "unlike" fractions, find equivalent fractions with the same denominator before you can add or subtract fractions with different denominators. Use this formula: $\frac{a}{b} - \frac{c}{d} = \frac{ad-cb}{bd}$

$\frac{3}{7} + \frac{2}{3} = \frac{(3)(3)+(2)(7)}{7 \times 3} = \frac{9+14}{21} = \frac{23}{21}$

✍ *Find the sum or difference.*

1) $\frac{4}{5} + \frac{2}{3} =$

2) $\frac{1}{4} + \frac{1}{3} =$

3) $\frac{3}{2} - \frac{1}{8} =$

4) $\frac{2}{5} - \frac{1}{3} =$

5) $\frac{3}{4} + \frac{5}{4} =$

6) $\frac{4}{7} + \frac{2}{3} =$

7) $\frac{4}{7} - \frac{1}{3} =$

8) $\frac{6}{7} - \frac{3}{5} =$

9) $\frac{3}{8} + \frac{1}{7} =$

Multiplying and Dividing Fractions

Step-by-step guide:

- ✓ Multiplying fractions: multiply the top numbers and multiply the bottom numbers.
- ✓ Dividing fractions: Keep, Change, Flip
- ✓ Keep first fraction, change division sign to multiplication, and flip the numerator and denominator of the second fraction. Then, solve!

Examples:

1) Multiplying fractions. $\frac{2}{5} \times \frac{3}{4} =$

Multiply the top numbers and multiply the bottom numbers.

$\frac{2}{5} \times \frac{3}{4} = \frac{2 \times 3}{5 \times 4} = \frac{6}{20}$, simplify: $\frac{6}{20} = \frac{6 \div 2}{20 \div 2} = \frac{3}{10}$

2) Dividing fractions. $\frac{1}{2} \div \frac{3}{5} =$

Keep first fraction, change division sign to multiplication, and flip the numerator and denominator of the second fraction. Then: $\frac{1}{2} \times \frac{5}{3} = \frac{1 \times 5}{2 \times 3} = \frac{5}{6}$

✎ *Find the answers.*

1) $\frac{1}{3} \times \frac{5}{4} =$

2) $\frac{1}{7} \times \frac{3}{4} =$

3) $\frac{1}{5} \div \frac{1}{4} =$

4) $\frac{3}{4} \div \frac{2}{3} =$

5) $\frac{5}{6} \times \frac{1}{4} =$

6) $\frac{3}{8} \times \frac{5}{9} =$

7) $\frac{3}{8} \div \frac{1}{5} =$

8) $\frac{6}{15} \div \frac{1}{2} =$

9) $\frac{2}{7} \div \frac{6}{5} =$

10) $\frac{4}{7} \times \frac{8}{9} =$

11) $\frac{1}{16} \times \frac{4}{5} =$

12) $\frac{8}{15} \div \frac{6}{5} =$

Adding Mixed Numbers

Step-by-step guide:

Use the following steps for both adding and subtracting mixed numbers.

- ✓ Add whole numbers of the mixed numbers.
- ✓ Add the fractions of each mixed number.
- ✓ Find the Least Common Denominator (LCD) if necessary.
- ✓ Add whole numbers and fractions.
- ✓ Write your answer in lowest terms.

Examples:

1) Add mixed numbers. $1\frac{1}{2} + 2\frac{2}{3} =$

Rewriting our equation with parts separated, $1 + \frac{1}{2} + 2 + \frac{2}{3}$, Solving the whole number parts $1 + 2 = 3$, Solving the fraction parts $\frac{1}{2} + \frac{2}{3}$, and rewrite to solve with the equivalent fractions.

$\frac{3}{6} + \frac{4}{6} = \frac{7}{6} = 1\frac{1}{6}$, then Combining the whole and fraction parts $3 + 1 + \frac{1}{6} = 4\frac{1}{6}$

2) Add mixed numbers. $2\frac{1}{4} + 1\frac{2}{5} =$

Rewriting our equation with parts separated, $2 + \frac{1}{4} + 1 + \frac{2}{5}$, Solving the whole number parts $2 + 1 = 3$, Solving the fraction parts $\frac{1}{4} + \frac{2}{5}$, and rewrite to solve with the equivalent fractions.

$\frac{5}{20} + \frac{8}{20} = \frac{13}{20}$, then Combining the whole and fraction parts $3 + \frac{13}{20} = 3\frac{13}{20}$

✍ *Find the sum.*

1) $1\frac{1}{2} + 2\frac{2}{3} =$

2) $2\frac{1}{3} + 1\frac{1}{2} =$

3) $1\frac{3}{5} + 2\frac{1}{4} =$

4) $3\frac{2}{5} + 2\frac{1}{3} =$

5) $1\frac{2}{7} + 1\frac{3}{4} =$

6) $3\frac{4}{5} + 2\frac{2}{7} =$

7) $2\frac{1}{2} + 7\frac{3}{8} =$

8) $2\frac{7}{8} + 1\frac{1}{3} =$

9) $2\frac{4}{9} + 6\frac{5}{12} =$

Subtract Mixed Numbers

Step-by-step guide:

Use the following steps for both adding and subtracting mixed numbers.

✓ Subtract the whole number of second mixed number from whole number of the first mixed number.
✓ Subtract the second fraction from the first one.
✓ Find the Least Common Denominator (LCD) if necessary.
✓ Add the result of whole numbers and fractions.
✓ Write your answer in lowest terms.

Examples:

1) Subtract. $2\frac{3}{5} - 1\frac{1}{3} =$

Rewriting our equation with parts separated, $2 + \frac{3}{5} - 1 - \frac{1}{3}$

Solving the whole number parts $2 - 1 = 1$, Solving the fraction parts, $\frac{3}{5} - \frac{1}{3} = \frac{9-5}{15} = \frac{4}{15}$

Combining the whole and fraction parts, $1 + \frac{4}{15} = 1\frac{4}{15}$

2) Subtract. $5\frac{5}{8} - 2\frac{1}{4} =$

Rewriting our equation with parts separated, $5 + \frac{5}{8} - 2 - \frac{1}{4}$

Solving the whole number parts $5 - 2 = 3$, Solving the fraction parts, $\frac{5}{8} - \frac{1}{4} = \frac{20-8}{32} = \frac{12}{32}$

Combining the whole and fraction parts, $3 + \frac{12}{32} = 3\frac{12}{32}$

✍ *Find the difference.*

1) $1\frac{2}{3} - 1\frac{1}{2} =$

2) $2\frac{1}{4} - 1\frac{1}{5} =$

3) $3\frac{3}{4} - 2\frac{2}{3} =$

4) $4\frac{5}{6} - 2\frac{2}{3} =$

5) $5\frac{3}{5} - 2\frac{1}{4} =$

6) $6\frac{3}{7} - 1\frac{2}{5} =$

7) $4\frac{4}{9} - 2\frac{2}{3} =$

8) $9\frac{3}{10} - 4\frac{1}{3} =$

9) $12\frac{3}{8} - 8\frac{5}{12} =$

Multiplying Mixed Numbers

Step-by-step guide:

✓ Convert the mixed numbers to improper fractions. (improper fraction is a fraction in which the top number is bigger than bottom number)

✓ Multiply fractions and simplify if necessary.

$$a\frac{c}{b} = a + \frac{c}{b} = \frac{ab + c}{b}$$

Examples:

1) Multiply mixed numbers. $2\frac{1}{4} \times 3\frac{1}{2} =$

Converting mixed numbers to fractions, $2\frac{1}{4} = \frac{9}{4}$ and $3\frac{1}{2} = \frac{7}{2}$.

$\frac{9}{4} \times \frac{7}{2}$, Applying the fractions formula for multiplication, $\frac{9 \times 7}{4 \times 2} = \frac{63}{8} = 7\frac{7}{8}$

2) Multiply mixed numbers. $5\frac{2}{3} \times 3\frac{3}{4} =$

Converting mixed numbers to fractions, $\frac{17}{3} \times \frac{15}{4}$, Applying the fractions formula for multiplication, $\frac{17 \times 15}{3 \times 4} = \frac{85}{4} = 21\frac{1}{4}$

✍ *Find the product.*

1) $1\frac{1}{2} \times 2\frac{1}{4} =$

2) $1\frac{2}{3} \times 1\frac{3}{4} =$

3) $4\frac{2}{5} \times 2\frac{1}{2} =$

4) $3\frac{1}{6} \times 1\frac{2}{3} =$

5) $3\frac{2}{7} \times 2\frac{1}{5} =$

6) $4\frac{2}{3} \times 3\frac{1}{7} =$

7) $5\frac{3}{8} \times 2\frac{3}{4} =$

8) $3\frac{4}{7} \times 7\frac{2}{9} =$

9) $8\frac{3}{5} \times 4\frac{3}{8} =$

10) $6\frac{5}{7} \times 2\frac{5}{9} =$

Dividing Mixed Numbers

Step-by-step guide:

- ✓ Convert the mixed numbers to improper fractions.

- ✓ Divide fractions and simplify if necessary.

$$a\frac{c}{b} = a + \frac{c}{b} = \frac{ab + c}{b}$$

Examples:

1) Find the quotient. $2\frac{1}{3} \div 1\frac{1}{4} =$

Converting mixed numbers to fractions, $\frac{7}{3} \div \frac{5}{4}$, Applying the fractions formula for multiplication, $\frac{7 \times 4}{3 \times 5} = \frac{28}{15} = 1\frac{13}{15}$

2) Find the quotient. $2\frac{5}{6} \div 1\frac{2}{5} =$

Converting mixed numbers to fractions, $\frac{17}{6} \div \frac{7}{5}$, Applying the fractions formula for multiplication, $\frac{17 \times 5}{6 \times 7} = \frac{85}{42} = 2\frac{1}{42}$

✍ *Find the quotient.*

1) $3\frac{1}{3} \div 2\frac{1}{2} =$

2) $2\frac{1}{2} \div 1\frac{1}{4} =$

3) $4\frac{3}{4} \div 2\frac{2}{3} =$

4) $3\frac{1}{6} \div 2\frac{2}{3} =$

5) $5\frac{1}{4} \div 2\frac{3}{5} =$

6) $2\frac{2}{7} \div 2\frac{1}{4} =$

7) $1\frac{4}{9} \div 2\frac{1}{3} =$

8) $7\frac{4}{5} \div 3\frac{2}{3} =$

9) $6\frac{3}{4} \div 2\frac{2}{5} =$

10) $8\frac{4}{7} \div 3\frac{5}{6} =$

Answers – Day 1

Simplifying Fractions

1) $\dfrac{4}{3}$

2) $\dfrac{1}{4}$

3) $\dfrac{1}{2}$

4) $\dfrac{3}{4}$

5) $\dfrac{2}{3}$

6) $\dfrac{1}{6}$

7) $\dfrac{1}{3}$

8) $\dfrac{11}{13}$

9) $\dfrac{14}{27}$

10) $\dfrac{7}{15}$

11) $\dfrac{7}{9}$

12) $\dfrac{19}{25}$

Adding and Subtracting Fractions

1) $\dfrac{22}{15}$

2) $\dfrac{7}{12}$

3) $\dfrac{11}{8}$

4) $\dfrac{1}{15}$

5) 2

6) $\dfrac{26}{21}$

7) $\dfrac{5}{21}$

8) $\dfrac{9}{35}$

9) $\dfrac{29}{56}$

Multiplying and Dividing Fractions

1) $\dfrac{5}{12}$

2) $\dfrac{3}{28}$

3) $\dfrac{4}{5}$

4) $\dfrac{9}{8}$

5) $\dfrac{5}{24}$

6) $\dfrac{5}{24}$

7) $\dfrac{15}{8}$

8) $\dfrac{4}{5}$

9) $\dfrac{5}{21}$

10) $\dfrac{32}{63}$

11) $\dfrac{1}{20}$

12) $\dfrac{4}{9}$

Adding Mixed Numbers

1) $4\dfrac{1}{6}$

2) $3\dfrac{5}{6}$

3) $3\dfrac{17}{20}$

4) $5\dfrac{11}{15}$

5) $3\dfrac{1}{28}$

6) $6\dfrac{3}{35}$

7) $9\dfrac{7}{8}$

8) $4\dfrac{5}{24}$

9) $8\dfrac{31}{36}$

Subtract Mixed Numbers

1) $\frac{1}{6}$

2) $1\frac{1}{20}$

3) $1\frac{1}{12}$

4) $2\frac{1}{6}$

5) $3\frac{7}{20}$

6) $5\frac{1}{35}$

7) $1\frac{7}{9}$

8) $4\frac{29}{30}$

9) $3\frac{23}{24}$

Multiplying Mixed Numbers

1) $3\frac{3}{8}$

2) $2\frac{11}{12}$

3) 11

4) $5\frac{5}{18}$

5) $7\frac{8}{35}$

6) $14\frac{2}{3}$

7) $14\frac{25}{32}$

8) $25\frac{50}{63}$

9) $37\frac{5}{8}$

10) $17\frac{10}{63}$

Dividing Mixed Numbers

1) $1\frac{1}{3}$

2) 2

3) $1\frac{25}{32}$

4) $1\frac{3}{16}$

5) $2\frac{1}{52}$

6) $1\frac{1}{63}$

7) $\frac{13}{21}$

8) $2\frac{7}{55}$

9) $2\frac{13}{16}$

10) $2\frac{38}{161}$

Chapter 2:
Decimals

Math Topics that you'll learn in this Chapter:

- ✓ Comparing Decimals

- ✓ Rounding Decimals

- ✓ Adding and Subtracting Decimals

- ✓ Multiplying and Dividing Decimals

"Do not worry about your difficulties in mathematics. I can assure you mine are still greater." ~ Albert Einstein

Comparing Decimals

Step-by-step guide:

Decimals: is a fraction written in a special form. For example, instead of writing $\frac{1}{2}$ you can write 0.5.

For comparing decimals:

✓ Compare each digit of two decimals in the same place value.
✓ Start from left. Compare hundreds, tens, ones, tenth, hundredth, etc.
✓ To compare numbers, use these symbols:
- Equal to =, Less than <, Greater than >
  Greater than or equal ≥, Less than or equal ≤

Examples:

1) Compare 0.40 and 0.04.

   0.40 *is greater than* 0.04, because the tenth place of 0.40 is 4, but the tenth place of 0.04 is zero. Then: $0.40 > 0.04$

2) Compare 0.0912 and 0.912.

   0.912 *is greater than* 0.0912, because the tenth place of 0.912 is 9, but the tenth place of 0.0912 is zero. Then: $0.0912 < 0.912$

✍ *Write the correct comparison symbol (>, < or =).*

1) 0.70 ☐ 0.070

2) 0.018 ☐ 0.18

3) 1.050 ☐ 1.05

4) 2.75 ☐ 2.07

5) 1.05 ☐ 0.550

6) 4.05 ☐ 4.5

7) 7.05 ☐ 7.050

8) 12.02 ☐ 12.1

9) 8.45 ☐ 8.125

10) 0.813 ☐ 0.0813

11) 14.15 ☐ 14.150

12) 0.678 ☐ 0.687

Rounding Decimals

Step-by-step guide:

- ✓ We can round decimals to a certain accuracy or number of decimal places. This is used to make calculation easier to do and results easier to understand, when exact values are not too important.
- ✓ First, you'll need to remember your place values: For example:

$$12.4567$$

1: tens	2: ones	4: tenths
5: hundredths	6: thousandths	7: tens thousandths

- ✓ To round a decimal, find the place value you'll round to.
- ✓ Find the digit to the right of the place value you're rounding to. If it is 5 or bigger, add 1 to the place value you're rounding to and remove all digits on its right side. If the digit to the right of the place value is less than 5, keep the place value and remove all digits on the right.

Examples:

1) Round 1.9278 to the thousandth place value.

First look at the next place value to the right, (tens thousandths). It's 8 and it is greater than 5. Thus add 1 to the digit in the thousandth place.

Thousandth place is 7. $\rightarrow 7 + 1 = 8$, then, the answer is 1.928

2) 9.4126 rounded to the nearest hundredth.

First look at the next place value to the right of thousandths. It's 2 and it is less than 5, thus remove all the digits to the right. Then, the answer is 9.41.

✎ *Round each decimal to the nearest whole number.*

1) 12.22	3) 11.45	5) 9.95
2) 9.5	4) 24.5	6) 77.8

✎ *Round each decimal to the nearest tenth.*

7) 14.352	9) 34.428	11) 1.7925
8) 10.569	10) 67.249	12) 23.319

Adding and Subtracting Decimals

Step-by-step guide:

- ✓ Line up the numbers.

- ✓ Add zeros to have same number of digits for both numbers if necessary.

- ✓ Add or subtract using column addition or subtraction.

Examples:

1) Add. $1.5 + 2.14 =$

First line up the numbers: $\begin{array}{r} 1.5 \\ + 2.14 \\ \hline \end{array}$ → Add zeros to have same number of digits for both

numbers. $\begin{array}{r} 1.50 \\ + 2.14 \\ \hline \end{array}$, Start with the hundredths place. $0 + 4 = 4$, $\begin{array}{r} 1.50 \\ + 2.14 \\ \hline 4 \end{array}$, Continue with tenths

place. $5 + 1 = 6$, $\begin{array}{r} 1.50 \\ + 2.14 \\ \hline .64 \end{array}$. Add the ones place. $2 + 1 = 3$, $\begin{array}{r} 1.50 \\ + 2.14 \\ \hline 3.64 \end{array}$

2) Subtract decimals. $2.56 - 1.15 = \begin{array}{r} 2.56 \\ - 1.15 \\ \hline \end{array}$

Start with the hundredths place. $6 - 5 = 1$, $\begin{array}{r} 2.56 \\ - 1.15 \\ \hline 1 \end{array}$, continue with tenths place. $5 - 1 = 4$

$\begin{array}{r} 2.56 \\ - 1.15 \\ \hline .41 \end{array}$, subtract the ones place. $2 - 1 = 1$, $\begin{array}{r} 2.56 \\ - 1.15 \\ \hline 1.41 \end{array}$.

✍ *Find the sum or difference.*

1) $18.24 - 12.20 =$

2) $21.50 + 17.77 =$

3) $13.98 + 11.78 =$

4) $66.34 - 48.50 =$

5) $53.12 + 15.25 =$

6) $78.90 - 23.61 =$

7) $82.24 - 65.55 =$

8) $93.75 + 82.63 =$

Multiplying and Dividing Decimals

Step-by-step guide:

For Multiplication:

✓ Ignore the decimal point and set up and multiply the numbers as you do with whole numbers.
Count the total number of decimal places in both of the factors.
Place the decimal point in the product.
For Division:

✓ If the divisor is not a whole number, move decimal point to right to make it a whole number. Do the same for dividend.
✓ Divide similar to whole numbers.

Examples:

1) Find the product. $0.60 \times 0.20 =$

Set up and multiply the numbers as you do with whole numbers. Line up the numbers: $\begin{smallmatrix}60\\ \times\,20\end{smallmatrix}$, Start with the ones place → $60 \times 0 = 0$, $\frac{\begin{smallmatrix}60\\ \times 20\end{smallmatrix}}{0}$, Continue with other digits → $60 \times 2 = 120$, $\frac{\begin{smallmatrix}60\\ \times 20\end{smallmatrix}}{1,200}$, Count the total number of decimal places in both of the factors. (4). Then Place the decimal point in the product.

Then: $\frac{\begin{smallmatrix}0.60\\ \times\,0.20\end{smallmatrix}}{0.1200}$ → $0.60 \times 0.20 = 0.12$

2) Find the quotient. $1.40 \div 0.2 =$

The divisor is not a whole number. Multiply it by 10 to get 2. Do the same for the dividend to get 14. Now, divide: $14 \div 2 = 7$. The answer is 7.

✍ *Find the product and quotient.*

1) $0.2 \times 0.5 =$	5) $1.12 \times 0.4 =$	9) $8.42 \div 2 =$
2) $1.5 \times 0.8 =$	6) $0.34 \times 0.5 =$	10) $8.6 \div 0.4 =$
3) $0.25 \times 0.5 =$	7) $2.25 \div 0.5 =$	11) $42.6 \div 0.2 =$
4) $0.15 \times 0.30 =$	8) $62.2 \div 1,000 =$	12) $86.5 \div 5 =$

Answers – Chapter 2

Comparing Decimals

1) >
2) <
3) =
4) >
5) >
6) <

7) =
8) <
9) >
10) >
11) =
12) <

Rounding Decimals

1) 12
2) 10
3) 11
4) 25

5) 10
6) 78
7) 14.4
8) 10.6

9) 34.4
10) 67.2
11) 1.8
12) 23.3

Adding and Subtracting Decimals

1) 6.04
2) 39.27
3) 25.76

4) 17.84
5) 68.37
6) 55.29

7) 16.69
8) 176.38

Multiplying and Dividing Decimals

1) 0.1
2) 1.2
3) 0.125
4) 0.045

5) 0.448
6) 0.17
7) 4.5
8) 0.0622

9) 4.21
10) 21.5
11) 213
12) 17.3

Chapter 3:
Factoring Numbers

Math Topics that you'll learn in this Chapter:

- ✓ Factoring Numbers

- ✓ Greatest Common Factor

- ✓ Least Common Multiple

"The study of mathematics, like the Nile, begins in minuteness but ends in magnificence."

- Charles Caleb Colton

Factoring Numbers

Step-by-step guide:

- ✓ Factoring numbers means to break the numbers into their prime factors.
- ✓ First few prime numbers: $2, 3, 5, 7, 11, 13, 17, 19$

Examples:

1) List all positive factors of 8.

   Write the upside-down division:
   The second column is the answer.
   Then: $8 = 2 \times 2 \times 2$ or $8 = 2^3$

8	2
4	2
2	2
1	

2) List all positive factors of 24.

   Write the upside-down division:
   The second column is the answer.
   Then: $24 = 2 \times 2 \times 2 \times 3$
   or $20 = 2^3 \times 3$

24	2
12	2
6	2
3	3
1	

✎ *List all positive factors of each number.*

1) 4	5) 16	9) 36
2) 6	6) 18	10) 38
3) 9	7) 24	11) 42
4) 12	8) 28	12) 56

Greatest Common Factor

Step-by-step guide:

- ✓ List the prime factors of each number.
- ✓ Multiply common prime factors.
- ✓ If there are no common prime factors, the GCF is 1.

Examples:

1) Find the GCF for 8 and 12.

The factors of 8 are: $\{1, 2, 4, 8\}$

The factors of 12 are: $\{1, 2, 3, 4, 6, 12\}$

There is 4 in common,

Then the greatest common factor is: 4.

2) Find the GCF for 14 and 18.

The factors of 8 are: $\{1, 2, 7, 14\}$

The factors of 20 are: $\{1, 2, 3, 6, 9, 18\}$

There is 2 in common.

Then the greatest common factor is: 2.

✎ *Find the GCF for each number pair.*

1) 6, 2	5) 4, 10	9) 15, 12
2) 4, 8	6) 6, 18	10) 14, 20
3) 5, 10	7) 9, 24	11) 12, 26
4) 8, 12	8) 16, 14	12) 22, 32

Least Common Multiple

Step-by-step guide:

- ✓ Least Common Multiple is the smallest multiple that 2 or more numbers have in common.
- ✓ How to find LCM: list out all the multiples of each number and then find the first one they have in common,

Examples:

1) Find the LCM for 8 and 6.

Multiples of 8: $8, 16, 24, ...$

Multiples of 6: $6, 12, 18, 24, ...$

$LCM = 24$

2) Find the LCM for 4 and 12.

Multiples of 4: $4, 8, 12, 16, 20, ...$

Multiples of 12: $12, 24, 36, 48$

$LCM = 12$

✎ *Find the LCM for each number pair.*

1) 2, 4	5) 8, 16	9) 6, 22
2) 3, 6	6) 12, 8	10) 14, 28
3) 6, 8	7) 4, 12	11) 16, 18
4) 7, 12	8) 5, 20	12) 24, 32

Answers – Chapter 3

Factoring Numbers

1) 2×2
2) 2×3
3) 3×3
4) $2 \times 2 \times 3$
5) $2 \times 2 \times 2 \times 2$
6) $2 \times 3 \times 3$

7) $2 \times 2 \times 2 \times 3$
8) $2 \times 2 \times 7$
9) $2 \times 2 \times 3 \times 3$
10) 2×19
11) $2 \times 3 \times 7$
12) $2 \times 2 \times 2 \times 7$

Greatest Common Factor

1) 2
2) 4
3) 5
4) 4
5) 2
6) 6

7) 3
8) 2
9) 3
10) 2
11) 2
12) 2

Least Common Multiple

1) 4
2) 6
3) 24
4) 84
5) 16
6) 24

7) 12
8) 20
9) 66
10) 28
11) 144
12) 96

Chapter 4:
Integers and Order of Operations

Math Topics that you'll learn in this Chapter:

- ✓ Adding and Subtracting Integers

- ✓ Multiplying and Dividing Integers

- ✓ Ordering Integers and Numbers

- ✓ Order of Operations

- ✓ Integers and Absolute Value

Without mathematics, there's nothing you can do. Everything around you is mathematics. Everything around you is numbers. " - Shakuntala Devi

Adding and Subtracting Integers

Step-by-step guide:

- ✓ Integers includes: zero, counting numbers, and the negative of the counting numbers. $\{... , -3, -2, -1, 0, 1, 2, 3, ...\}$
- ✓ Add a positive integer by moving to the right on the number line.
- ✓ Add a negative integer by moving to the left on the number line.
- ✓ Subtract an integer by adding its opposite.

Examples:

1) Solve. $(-2) - (-6) =$

Keep the first number, and convert the sign of the second number to it's opposite. (change subtraction into addition. Then: $(-2) + 6 = 4$

2) Solve. $8 + (12 - 20) =$

First subtract the numbers in brackets, $12 - 20 = -8$

Then: $8 + (-8) = \rightarrow$ change addition into subtraction: $8 - 8 = 0$

✍ *Find each sum or difference.*

1) $-(2) + 9 =$

2) $(-4) + (-8) =$

3) $12 + (-18) =$

4) $13 + (-22) =$

5) $2 + (-9) + 3 =$

6) $(-18) + (-4) + 2 =$

7) $4 + (-2) - (-8) =$

8) $5 - (-20 - 12) =$

9) $(-4 + 2) - 6 =$

10) $10 - (-6 + 5) =$

11) $15 - (5 - 3) =$

12) $-(22) - (-13) + 4 =$

Multiplying and Dividing Integers

Step-by-step guide:

Use these rules for multiplying and dividing integers:
- ✓ (negative) × (negative) = positive
- ✓ (negative) ÷ (negative) = positive
- ✓ (negative) × (positive) = negative
- ✓ (negative) ÷ (positive) = negative
- ✓ (positive) × (positive) = positive

Examples:

1) Solve. $3 \times (12 - 14) =$

First subtract the numbers in brackets, $12 - 14 = -2 \rightarrow (3) \times (-2) =$

Now use this formula: (negative) × (positive) = negative
$(3) \times (-2) = -6$

2) Solve. $(-8) + (12 \div 4) =$

First divided 48 by 6 , the numbers in brackets, $12 \div 4 = 3$

$= (-8) + (3) = -8 + 3 = -5$

✎ *Find each product or quotient.*

1) $(-2) \times (9) =$

2) $(-12) \times 3 =$

3) $(-5) \times (-8) =$

4) $(-3) \times (-10) =$

5) $(-4) \times (-3) \times 2 =$

6) $(18 - 3) \times (-5) =$

7) $(16 - 4) \div (-4) =$

8) $(-15) \div (-3) =$

9) $(-48) \div (-6) =$

10) $56 \div (-8) =$

11) $(-121) \div 11 =$

12) $(-128) \div (-4) =$

Ordering Integers and Numbers

Step-by-step guide:

- ✓ When using a number line, numbers increase as you move to the right.
- ✓ When comparing two numbers, think about their position on number line. If one number is on the right side of another number, it is a bigger number. For example, -3 is bigger than -5 because it is on the right side of -5 on number line.

Examples:

1) Order this set of integers from least to greatest. $-4, -1, -5, 4, 2, 7$
The smallest number is -5 and the largest number is 7.

Now compare the integers and order them from least to greatest:
$-5 < -4 < -1 < 2 < 4 < 7$

2) Order each set of integers from greatest to least. $3, -2, -1, 6, -9, 8$
The largest number is 8 and the smallest number is -9.

Now compare the integers and order them from greatest to least:
$8 > 6 > 3 > -1 > -2 > -9$

✍ *Order each set of integers from least to greatest.*

1) $6, -8, -5, 0, 2$ ___, ___, ___, ___, ___, ___
2) $-3, -10, 4, 11, 8$ ___, ___, ___, ___, ___, ___
3) $17, -11, -18, 20, -19$ ___, ___, ___, ___, ___, ___
4) $-14, -24, 17, -6, 31$ ___, ___, ___, ___, ___, ___

✍ *Order each set of integers from greatest to least.*

5) $10, 15, -8, -11, -5$ ___, ___, ___, ___, ___, ___
6) $22, 30, -13, -19, 38$ ___, ___, ___, ___, ___, ___
7) $44, -20, -17, 54, -4$ ___, ___, ___, ___, ___, ___
8) $67, 80, -13, -9, 93$ ___, ___, ___, ___, ___, ___

Order of Operations

Step-by-step guide:

When there is more than one math operation, use PEMDAS:

- ✓ Parentheses
- ✓ Exponents
- ✓ Multiplication and Division (from left to right)
- ✓ Addition and Subtraction (from left to right)

Examples:

1) Solve. $(2 + 4) \div (2^2 \div 4) =$

First simplify inside parentheses: $(6) \div (4 \div 4) = (6) \div (1) =$
Then: $(6) \div (1) = 6$

2) Solve. $(9 \times 6) - (10 - 6) =$

First simplify inside parentheses: $(9 \times 6) - (10 - 6) = (54) - (4) =$

Then: $(54) - (4) = 50$

✍ *Evaluate each expression.*

1) $12 + (3 \times 2) =$

2) $8 - (4 \times 5) =$

3) $(8 \times 2) + 14 =$

4) $(10 - 6) - (4 \times 3) =$

5) $15 + (12 \div 2) =$

6) $(24 \times 3) \div 4 =$

7) $(28 \div 2) \times (-4) =$

8) $(2 \times 6) + (14 - 8) =$

9) $45 + (4 \times 2) + 12 =$

10) $(10 \times 5) \div (4 + 1) =$

11) $(-6) + (8 \times 6) + 10 =$

12) $(12 \times 4) - (56 \div 4) =$

Integers and Absolute Value

Step-by-step guide:

✓ To find an absolute value of a number, just find its distance from 0 on number line! For example, the distance of 12 and -12 from zero on number line is 12!

Examples:

1) Solve. $|8 - 2| \times \frac{|-4 \times 6|}{3} =$

First solve $|8 - 2|$, $\rightarrow |8 - 2| = |6|$, the absolute value of 6 is 6, $|6| = 6$

$6 \times \frac{|-4 \times 6|}{3} =$

Now solve $|-4 \times 6|$, $\rightarrow |-4 \times 6| = |-24|$, the absolute value of -24 is 24, $|-24| = 24$

Then: $6 \times \frac{24}{3} = 6 \times 8 = 48$

2) Solve. $\frac{|-1|}{3} \times |9 - 4| =$

First find $|-12|$, $\rightarrow$ the absolute value of -12 is 12, then: $|-12| = 12$

$\frac{12}{3} \times |9 - 4| =$

Next, solve $|9 - 4|$, $\rightarrow |9 - 4| = |-5|$, the absolute value of -5 is 5. $|-5| = 5$

Then: $\frac{12}{3} \times 5 = 4 \times 5 = 20$

✎ *Evaluate the value.*

1) $2 - |4 - 10| - |8| =$

2) $|7| - \frac{|-14|}{2} =$

3) $\frac{|-18|}{3} \times |-4| =$

4) $\frac{|6 \times -4|}{2} \times \frac{|-28|}{4} =$

5) $|12 \times -2| + \frac{|-56|}{7} =$

6) $\frac{|-40|}{4} \times \frac{|-6|}{11} =$

7) $|-25 + 3| \times \frac{|-8 \times 5|}{2} =$

8) $\frac{|20 \times -3|}{2} \times |-14| =$

Answers – Chapter 4

Adding and Subtracting Integers

1) 7
2) −12
3) −6
4) −9

5) −4
6) −20
7) 10
8) 37

9) −8
10) 11
11) 13
12) −5

Multiplying and Dividing Integers

1) −18
2) −36
3) 40
4) 30

5) 24
6) −75
7) −3
8) 5

9) 8
10) −7
11) −11
12) 32

Ordering Integers and Numbers

1) −8, −5, 0, 2, 6
2) −10, −3, 4, 8, 11
3) −19, −18, −11, 17, 20
4) −24, −14, −6, 17, 31

5) 15, 10, −5, −8, −11
6) 38, 30, 22, −13, −19
7) 54, 44, −4, −17, −20
8) 93, 80, 67, −9, −13

Order of Operations

1) 18
2) −12
3) 30
4) −8

5) 21
6) 18
7) −56
8) 18

9) 65
10) 10
11) 52
12) 34

Integers and Absolute Value

1) −12
2) 0
3) 24

4) 84
5) 32
6) 60

7) 440
8) 420

Chapter 5:
Ratios

Math Topics that you'll learn in this Chapter:

✓ Simplifying Ratios

✓ Proportional Ratios

✓ Create a Proportion

✓ Similarity and Ratios

✓ Simple Interest

Mathematics is the door and key to the sciences. ~ Roger Bacon

Simplifying Ratios

Step-by-step guide:

- ✓ Ratios are used to make comparisons between two numbers.
- ✓ Ratios can be written as a fraction, using the word "to", or with a colon.
- ✓ You can calculate equivalent ratios by multiplying or dividing both sides of the ratio by the same number.

Examples:

1) Simplify. $4:2 =$

Both numbers 4 and 2 are divisible by 2 , $\Rightarrow 4 \div 2 = 2, 2 \div 2 = 1$,

Then: $4:2 = 2:1$

2) Simplify. $\frac{14}{24} =$

Both numbers 14 and 24 are divisible by 2, $\Rightarrow 14 \div 2 = 7, 24 \div 2 = 12$,

Then: $\frac{14}{24} = \frac{7}{12}$

✍ *Reduce each ratio.*

1) $4:8 = $ ___ : ___

2) $5:10 = $ ___ : ___

3) $3:9 = $ ___ : ___

4) $8:6 = $ ___ : ___

5) $6:14 = $ ___ : ___

6) $5:25 = $ ___ : ___

7) $16:18 = $ ___ : ___

8) $30:40 = $ ___ : ___

9) $15:50 = $ ___ : ___

10) $14:18 = $ ___ : ___

11) $15:27 = $ ___ : ___

12) $48:24 = $ ___ : ___

Proportional Ratios

Step-by-step guide:

- ✓ A proportion means that two ratios are equal. It can be written in two ways:
  $\frac{a}{b} = \frac{c}{d}$, $a : b = c : d$

- ✓ The proportion $\frac{a}{b} = \frac{c}{d}$ can be written as: $a \times d = c \times b$

Examples:

1) Solve this proportion for x. $\frac{2}{4} = \frac{3}{x}$

   Use cross multiplication: $\frac{2}{4} = \frac{3}{x} \Rightarrow 2 \times x = 3 \times 4 \Rightarrow 2x = 12$

   Divide to find x: $\quad x = \frac{12}{2} \Rightarrow x = 6$

2) If a box contains red and blue balls in ratio of $2 : 5$ red to blue, how many red balls are there if 60 blue balls are in the box?

   Write a proportion and solve. $\frac{2}{5} = \frac{x}{60}$

   Use cross multiplication: $2 \times 60 = 5 \times x \Rightarrow 120 = 5x$

   Divide to find x: $\quad\quad\quad x = \frac{120}{5} \Rightarrow x = 24$

✎ *Solve each proportion.*

1) $\frac{2}{4} = \frac{8}{x}$, $x =$ _____

2) $\frac{1}{2} = \frac{6}{x}$, $x =$ _____

3) $\frac{2}{3} = \frac{12}{x}$, $x =$ _____

4) $\frac{1}{4} = \frac{x}{20}$, $x =$ _____

5) $\frac{3}{4} = \frac{x}{8}$, $x =$ _____

6) $\frac{1}{4} = \frac{18}{x}$, $x =$ _____

7) $\frac{5}{8} = \frac{10}{x}$, $x =$ _____

8) $\frac{6}{9} = \frac{24}{x}$, $x =$ _____

9) $\frac{4}{6} = \frac{x}{18}$, $x =$ _____

10) $\frac{5}{8} = \frac{x}{112}$, $x =$ _____

11) $\frac{3}{18} = \frac{x}{120}$, $x =$ _____

12) $\frac{12}{18} = \frac{x}{96}$, $x =$ _____

Create a Proportion

Step-by-step guide:

- ✓ A proportion contains two equal fractions! A proportion simply means that two fractions are equal.
- ✓ To create a proportion, simply find (or create) two equal fractions.

Examples:

1) Express ratios as a Proportion.

180 miles on 9 gallons of gas, how many miles on 1 gallon of gas?

First create a fraction: $\frac{180\ miles}{9\ gallons}$, and divide: $180 \div 9 = 20$

Then: 20 miles per gallon

2) State if this pair of ratios form a proportion. $\frac{2}{3}\ and\ \frac{12}{30}$

Use cross multiplication: $\frac{2}{3} = \frac{12}{30} \rightarrow 2 \times 30 = 12 \times 3 \rightarrow 60 = 36$, which is not correct.
Therefore, this pair of ratios doesn't form a proportion.

✎ *State if each pair of ratios form a proportion.*

1) $\frac{2}{10}\ and\ \frac{4}{20}$

2) $\frac{1}{2}\ and\ \frac{15}{25}$

3) $\frac{4}{9}\ and\ \frac{40}{81}$

4) $\frac{6}{11}\ and\ \frac{42}{77}$

5) $\frac{1}{6}\ and\ \frac{8}{48}$

6) $\frac{5}{6}\ and\ \frac{35}{42}$

7) $\frac{3}{7}\ and\ \frac{27}{72}$

8) $\frac{2}{5}\ and\ \frac{16}{45}$

9) $\frac{6}{17}\ and\ \frac{36}{85}$

10) $\frac{2}{7}\ and\ \frac{24}{86}$

11) $\frac{13}{21}\ and\ \frac{182}{294}$

12) $\frac{12}{19}\ and\ \frac{156}{247}$

Similarity and Ratios

Step-by-step guide:

✓ Two or more figures are similar if the corresponding angles are equal, and the corresponding sides are in proportion.

Examples:

1) A girl 180 cm tall, stands 340 cm from a lamp post at night. Her shadow from the light is 80 cm long. How high is the lamp post?

Write the proportion and solve for missing side.

$$\frac{\text{Smaller triangle height}}{\text{Smaller triangle base}} = \frac{\text{Bigger triangle height}}{\text{Bigger triangle base}}$$

$$\Rightarrow \frac{80cm}{180cm} = \frac{80+340cm}{x} \Rightarrow 80x = 180 \times 420 \Rightarrow x = 945 \ cm$$

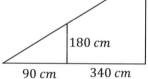

180 cm

90 cm 340 cm

2) A tree 20 $feet$ tall casts a shadow 14 $feet$ long. Jack is 10 $feet$ tall. How long is Jack's shadow?

Write a proportion and solve for the missing number.

$$\frac{20}{14} = \frac{10}{x} \rightarrow 20x = 10 \times 14$$

$$20x = 140 \rightarrow x = \frac{140}{20} = 7$$

✍ *Each pair of figures is similar. Find the missing side.*

1)

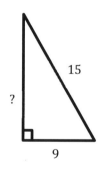

2)

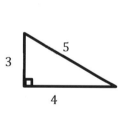

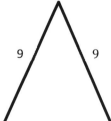

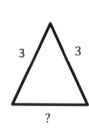

3)

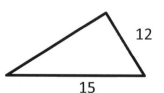

4)

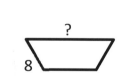

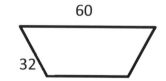

Simple Interest

Step-by-step guide:

✓ Simple Interest: The charge for borrowing money or the return for lending it. To solve a simple interest problem, use this formula:

Interest = principal x rate x time ⇒ $I = p \times r \times t$

Examples:

1) Find simple interest for $450 investment at 7% for 8 years.

Use Interest formula: $I = prt$

$P = \$450, r = 7\% = \frac{7}{100} = 0.07$ and $t = 8$

Then: $I = 450 \times 0.07 \times 8 = \$252$

2) Find simple interest for $5,200 at 4% for 3 years.

Use Interest formula: $I = prt$

$P = \$5,200, r = 4\% = \frac{4}{100} = 0.04$ and $t = 3$

Then: $I = 5,200 \times 0.04 \times 3 = \$624$

✎ *Determine the simple interest for these loans.*

1) $840 at 6% for 4 years. $ _____

2) $2,500 at 2% for 8 years. $ _____

3) $1,200 at 4% for 5 years. $ _____

4) $4,000 at 1.5% for 3 years. $ _____

5) $5,300 at 3% for 2 years. $ _____

6) $1,200 at 5.5% for 4 years. $ _____

7) $1,800 at 5% for 6 months. $ _____

8) $20,000 at 2.5% for 7 years. $ _____

Answers – Chapter 5

Simplifying Ratios

1) $1:2$
2) $1:2$
3) $1:3$
4) $4:3$

5) $3:7$
6) $1:5$
7) $8:9$
8) $3:4$

9) $3:10$
10) $7:9$
11) $5:9$
12) $2:1$

Proportional Ratios

1) 16
2) 12
3) 18
4) 5

5) 6
6) 72
7) 16
8) 36

9) 12
10) 70
11) 20
12) 96

Create a Proportion

1) Yes
2) No
3) No
4) Yes

5) Yes
6) Yes
7) Yes
8) *No*

9) No
10) No
11) Yes
12) Yes

Similarity and ratios

1) 12
2) 2

3) 5
4) 15

Simple Interest

1) $201.60
2) $400
3) $240
4) $180

5) $318
6) $264
7) $45
8) $3,500

Chapter 6:

Percentage

Math Topics that you'll learn in this Chapter:

- ✓ Percentage Calculations

- ✓ Percent Problems

- ✓ Percent of Increase and Decrease

- ✓ Discount, Tax and Tip

Mathematics is no more computation than typing is literature.

- John Allen Paulos

Percentage Calculations

Step-by-step guide:

- ✓ Percent is a ratio of a number and 100. It always has the same denominator, 100. Percent symbol is %.
- ✓ Percent is another way to write decimals or fractions. For example:
$$40\% = 0.40 = \frac{40}{100} = \frac{2}{5}$$
- ✓ Use the following formula to find part, whole, or percent:
$$\text{part} = \frac{\text{percent}}{100} \times \text{whole}$$

Examples:

1) What is 15% of 50? Use the following formula: $\text{part} = \frac{\text{percent}}{100} \times \text{whole}$

$$\text{part} = \frac{15}{100} \times 50 \rightarrow \text{part} = \frac{15 \times 50}{100} \rightarrow \text{part} = \frac{75}{10} \rightarrow \text{part} = 7.5$$

2) What is 30% of 35? Use the percent formula: $part = \frac{percent}{100} \times whole$

$$\text{part} = \frac{30}{100} \times 35 \rightarrow \text{part} = \frac{105}{10} \rightarrow \text{part} = 10.5$$

✍ *Calculate the given percent of each value.*

1) 10% of 100 = ____

2) 50% of 40 = ____

3) 20% of 50 = ____

4) 30% of 70 = ____

5) 45% of 20 = ____

6) 50% of 80 = ____

7) 30% of 100 = ____

8) 15% of 60 = ____

9) 40% of 90 = ____

10) 29% of 86 = ____

11) 33% of 54 = ____

12) 71% of 112 = ____

Percent Problems

Step-by-step guide:

✓ In each percent problem, we are looking for the base, or part or the percent.
✓ Use the following equations to find each missing section.
  ○ Base = Part ÷ Percent
  ○ Part = Percent × Base
  ○ Percent = Part ÷ Base

Examples:

1) 2.5 is what percent of 20?

In this problem, we are looking for the percent. Use the following equation:
$$Percent = Part \div Base \rightarrow Percent = 2.5 \div 20 = 0.125 = 12.5\%$$

2) 40 is 10% of what number?

Use the following formula: $Base = Part \div Percent \rightarrow Base = 40 \div 0.10 = 400$
40 is 10% of 400.

✍ **Solve each problem.**

1) 20 is what percent of 200? ____%

2) 40 is what percent of 50? ____%

3) 30 is 15 percent of what number? ____

4) 18 is 6 percent of what? ____

5) 20 is what percent of 50? ____%

6) 18 is what percent of 90? ____%

7) 25 is what percent of 80? ____%

8) 60 is what percent of 300? ____%

9) 50 is 20 percent of what number? ____

10) 68 *is* 16 *percent of what?* ___

11) 15 *is* 25 *percent of what?* ___

12) 80 *is* 25 *percent of what?* ___

Percent of Increase and Decrease

Step-by-step guide:

To find the percentage of increase or decrease:
- ✓ New Number – Original Number
- ✓ The result ÷ Original Number × 100
- ✓ If your answer is a negative number, then this is a percentage decrease. If it is positive, then this is a percent of increase.

Examples:

1) Increased by 20%, the numbers 30 becomes:

   First find 20% of 30 → $\frac{20}{100} \times 30 = \frac{20 \times 30}{100} = 6$

   Then: $30 + 6 = 36$

2) The price of a shirt increases from \$10 to \$15. What is the percent increase?
   First: $15 - 10 = 5$
   5 is the result. Then: $5 \div 10 = \frac{5}{10} = 0.5 = 50\%$

✍ *Solve each percent of change word problem.*

1) Bob got a raise, and his hourly wage increased from \$20 to \$25. What is the percent increase? _____ %

2) The price of a pair of shoes increases from \$18 to \$27. What is the percent increase? _____ %

3) At a coffeeshop, the price of a cup of coffee increased from \$1.50 to \$1.80. What is the percent increase in the cost of the coffee? _____ %

4) 4 *cm* are cut from a 20 *cm* board. What is the percent decrease in length? _____ %

5) In a class, the number of students has been increased from 25 to 29. What is the percent increase? _____ %

6) The price of gasoline rose from \$2.60 to \$2.86 in one month. By what percent did the gas price rise? _____ %

7) A shirt was originally priced at \$48. It went on sale for \$38.40. What was the percent that the shirt was discounted? _____ %

Discount, Tax and Tip

Step-by-step guide:

- ✓ Discount = Multiply the regular price by the rate of discount
- ✓ Selling price = original price – discount
- ✓ Tax: To find tax, multiply the tax rate to the taxable amount (income, property value, etc.)
- ✓ To find tip, multiply the rate to the selling price.

Examples:

1) With an 20% discount, Ella was able to save $40 on a dress. What was the original price of the dress?

$20\% \ of \ x = \ 40, \frac{20}{100} \times x = 40, x = \frac{100 \times 40}{20} = 200$

2) Sophia purchased a sofa for $250.40. The sofa is regularly priced at $313.125. What was the percent discount Sophia received on the sofa?

Use this formula: $percent = Part \div base = 250.50 \div 313.125 = 0.80 = 80\%$

Therefore, the discount is: $100\% - 80\% = 20\%$

✎ *Find the selling price of each item.*

1) Original price of a computer: $200

   Tax: 10%, Selling price: $_____

2) Original price of a laptop: $400

   Tax: 5%, Selling price: $_____

3) Original price of a sofa: $500

   Tax: 8%, Selling price: $_____

4) Original price of a car: $800

   Tax: 25%, Selling price: $_____

5) Original price of a Table: $250

   Tax: 10%, Selling price: $_____

6) Original price of a house: $1,500

   Tax: 15%   Selling price: $_____

7) Original price of a tablet: $600

   Discount: 20%, Selling price: $_____

8) Original price of a chair: $450

   Discount: 25%, Selling price: $_____

9) Original price of a book: $125

   Discount: 15%, Selling price: $_____

10) Original price of a cellphone: $900

   Discount: 12%, Selling price: $_____

Answers – Chapter 6

Percentage Calculations

1) 10	5) 9	9) 36
2) 20	6) 40	10) 24.94
3) 10	7) 30	11) 17.82
4) 21	8) 9	12) 79.52

Percent Problems

1) 10%	5) 40%	9) 250%
2) 80%	6) 20%	10) 425
3) 200	7) 31.25%	11) 60
4) 300	8) 20%	12) 320

Percent of Increase and Decrease

1) 25%	5) 16%
2) 50%	6) 10%
3) 20%	7) 20%
4) 20%	

Markup, Discount, and Tip

1) $220.00	6) $1,725
2) $420.00	7) $480.00
3) $540.00	8) $337.50
4) $1,000.00	9) $106.25
5) $275.00	10) $792.00

Chapter 7:
Exponents and Variables

Math Topics that you'll learn in this Chapter:

- ✓ Simplifying Variable Expressions
- ✓ Simplifying Polynomial Expressions
- ✓ Translate Phrases into an Algebraic Statement
- ✓ The Distributive Property
- ✓ Evaluating One Variable
- ✓ Evaluating Two Variables
- ✓ Combining like Terms

Mathematics is, as it were, a sensuous logic, and relates to philosophy as do the arts, music, and plastic art to poetry. – K.

Shegel

Simplifying Variable Expressions

Step-by-step guide:

- ✓ In algebra, a variable is a letter used to stand for a number. The most common letters are: $x, y, z, a, b, c, m,$ and n.
- ✓ algebraic expression is an expression contains integers, variables, and the math operations such as addition, subtraction, multiplication, division, etc.
- ✓ In an expression, we can combine "like" terms. (values with same variable and same power)

Examples:

1) Simplify this expression. $(2x + 3x + 4) =$?
   Combine like terms. Then: $(2x + 3x + 4) = 5x + 4$ (remember you cannot combine variables and numbers.
2) Simplify this expression. $12 - 3x^2 + 5x + 4x^2 =$?
   Combine "like" terms: $-3x^2 + 4x^2 = x^2$

   Then: $= 12 + x^2 + 5x$. Write in standard form (biggest powers first): $x^2 + 5x + 12$

✎ *Simplify each expression.*

1) $x - 4 + 6 - 2x =$

2) $3 - 4x + 14 - 3x =$

3) $33x - 5 + 13 + 4x =$

4) $-3 - x^2 - 7x^2 =$

5) $4 + 11x^2 + 3 =$

6) $7x^2 + 5x + 6x^2 =$

7) $42x + 15 + 3x^2 =$

8) $6x(x - 2) - 5 =$

9) $7x - 6 + 9x + 3x^2 =$

10) $(-5)(7x - 2) + 12x =$

11) $15x - 6(6 - 7x) =$

12) $25x + 6(7x + 2) + 14 =$

Simplifying Polynomial Expressions

Step-by-step guide:

✓ In mathematics, a polynomial is an expression consisting of variables and coefficients that involves only the operations of addition, subtraction, multiplication, and non-negative integer exponents of variables.

$$P(x) = a_n x^n + a_{n-1} x^{n-1} + \dots + a_2 x^2 + a_1 x + a_0$$

Examples:

1) Simplify this Polynomial Expressions. $x^2 - 5x^3 + 2x^4 - 4x^3 =$
   Combine "like" terms: $-5x^3 - 4x^3 = -9x^3$
   Then: $x^2 - 5x^3 + 2x^4 - 4x^3 = x^2 - 9x^3 + 2x^4$
   Then write in standard form: $= 2x^4 - 9x^3 + x^2$

2) Simplify this expression. $(2x^2 - x^3) - (x^3 - 4x^2) =$
   First use distributive property: → multiply $(-)$ into $(x^3 - 4x^2)$
   $(2x^2 - x^3) - (x^3 - 4x^2) = 2x^2 - x^3 - x^3 + 4x^2$
   Then combine "like" terms: $2x^2 - x^3 - x^3 + 4x^2 = 6x^2 - 2x^3$
   And write in standard form: $= -2x^3 + 6x^2$

✎ *Simplify each polynomial.*

1) $4x^2 + 7x^3 - 9x^2 + 15x =$ _____

2) $3x^4 - 6x^5 + 7x^4 - 9x^2 =$ _____

3) $6x^3 + 18x - x^2 - 3x^3 =$ _____

4) $3x^3 - (5x^4 + 3x) + x^2 =$ _____

5) $x^4 - 3(x^2 + x) + 2x =$ _____

6) $(6x^3 - 4) + 3(4x^2 - 2x^3) =$ _____

7) $(5x^3 - 3x) - 3(6x^3 - 4x^4) =$ _____

8) $3(6x - 2x^3) - 4(2x^3 + 3x^2) =$ _____

Translate Phrases into an Algebraic Statement

Step-by-step guide:

Translating key words and phrases into algebraic expressions:

- ✓ Addition: plus, more than, the sum of, etc.
- ✓ Subtraction: minus, less than, decreased, etc.
- ✓ Multiplication: times, product, multiplied, etc.
- ✓ Division: quotient, divided, ratio, etc.

Examples:

Write an algebraic expression for each phrase.

1) 12 times the sum of 5 and x.

   Sum of 5 and x: $5 + x$. Times means multiplication. Then: $12 \times (5 + x)$

2) Nine more than a number is 18.

   More than mean plus a number $= x$

   Then: $9 + x = 18$

✎ *Write an algebraic expression for each phrase.*

1) 9 decreased by y. _____

2) Add y to 16. _____

3) The square of 8. _____

4) 7 multiplied by x. _____

5) Subtract 22 from y. _____

6) 13 divided by x. _____

7) x raised to the fifth power. _____

8) The sum of five and a number. _____

9) The difference between fifty–four and y. _____

10) The quotient of eleven and a number. _____

11) The quotient of the square of b and 8. _____

12) The difference between x and 24 is 18. _____

The Distributive Property

Step-by-step guide:

✓ Distributive Property:
$$a(b + c) = ab + ac$$

Examples:

1) **Simply.** $(-2)(x - 3) =$

Use Distributive Property formula: $a(b + c) = ab + ac$
$(-2)(x - 3) = -2x + 6$

2) **Simply**$(5)(6x - 3) =$

Use Distributive Property formula: $a(b + c) = ab + ac$
$(5)(6x - 3) = 30x - 15$

✎ *Use the distributive property to simply each expression.*

1) $(-4)(x - 7) =$

2) $-(8 - 5x) =$

3) $7(7 + 3x) =$

4) $3(14 + 3x) =$

5) $(-7x + 6)3 =$

6) $6(5 + 7x) =$

7) $12(4x + 3) =$

8) $(-3x + 5)5 =$

9) $(5 - 8x)(-9) =$

10) $(-4)(2 - 16x) =$

11) $12(4x - 15) =$

12) $(-15x + 20)(-2) =$

Evaluating One Variable

Step-by-step guide:

- ✓ To evaluate one variable expression, find the variable and substitute a number for that variable.
- ✓ Perform the arithmetic operations.

Examples:

1) **Solve this expression.** $18 - 2x$, $x = 2$

First substitute 2 for x, then:

$18 - 2x = 18 - 2(2) = 18 - 4 = 14$

2) **Solve this expression.** $5 - 2x$, $x = -1$

First substitute -1 for x, then:

$5 - 2x = 5 - 2(-1) = 5 + 2 = 7$

✍ *Evaluate each expression using the value given.*

1) $3x - 6$, $x = 3$

2) $6x + 5$, $x = -2$

3) $10 - x$, $x = 2$

4) $x + 3$, $x = 4$

5) $2x + 6$, $x = 7$

6) $12 - 2x$, $x = -3$

7) $4x + 5$, $x = 3$

8) $5x + 7$, $x = -2$

9) $12 + 3x - 7$, $x = 2$

10) $6(5x + 3)$, $x = 7$

11) $3(-6x - 3)$, $x = 4$

12) $8x - 4x + 14$, $x = 5$

Evaluating Two Variables

Step-by-step guide:

✓ To evaluate an algebraic expression, substitute a number for each variable and perform the arithmetic operations.

Examples:

1) **Solve this expression.** $4(2a - b), a = 2, b = -1$

First substitute 2 for a, and -1 for b , then:

$4(2a - b), 8a - 4b = 8(2) - 4(-1) = 16 + 4 = 20$

2) **Solve this expression.** $2x + 6y , x = 1, y = 2$

First substitute 1 for x, and 2 for y , then:

$2x + 6y = 2(1) + 6(2) = 2 + 12 = 14$

✎ *Evaluate each expression using the values given.*

1) $x + 2y,$
   $x = 1, y = 2$

2) $2x - 3y,$
   $x = 1, y = -2$

3) $-a + 5b,$
   $a = -2, b = 3$

4) $-3a + 5b,$
   $a = 5, b = 2$

5) $5x + 8 - 3y,$
   $x = 5, y = 4$

6) $3x + 5y,$
   $x = 2, y = 3$

7) $7x + 6y,$
   $x = 2, y = 4$

8) $3a - (12 - b),$
   $a = 3, b = 5$

9) $4z + 20 + 7k,$
   $z = -4, k = 5$

10) $xy + 15 + 4x,$
    $x = 6, y = 3$

11) $8x + 3 - 5y + 4,$
    $x = 6, y = 3$

12) $5 + 2(-3x - 4y),$
    $x = 6, y = 5$

Combining like Terms

Step-by-step guide:

- ✓ Terms are separated by "+" and "-" signs.
- ✓ Like terms are terms with same variables and same powers.
- ✓ Be sure to use the "+" or "-" that is in front of the coefficient.

Examples:

1) **Simplify this expression.** $(-2)(2x - 2) =$

First use Distributive Property formula: $a(b + c) = ab + ac$
$(-2)(2x - 2) = -4x + 4$

2) **Simplify this expression.** $4(-2x + 6) =$

Use Distributive Property formula: $a(b + c) = a + ac$
$4(-2x + 6) = -8x + 24$

✎ *Simplify each expression.*

1) $-4x + x + 5 =$

2) $-2(3x - 4) =$

3) $-14x + 6 - 12x =$

4) $8x - 12 - 3x + 3 =$

5) $13x + 5x - 22 =$

6) $3(4x + 8) + 7x =$

7) $3(5 - 2x) - 20x =$

8) $-5x - (7 - 15x) =$

9) $5(-15x + 3) - 17x =$

10) $-8x - 23 + 19x =$

11) $24x - 13x + 8 - 6x =$

12) $(-3)(8x - 5) - 19x =$

Answers – Chapter 7

Simplifying Variable Expressions

1) $-x + 2$
2) $-7x + 17$
3) $37x + 8$
4) $-8x^2 - 3$
5) $11x^2 + 7$
6) $13x^2 + 5x$

7) $3x^2 + 42x + 15$
8) $6x^2 - 12x - 5$
9) $3x^2 + 16x - 6$
10) $-23x + 10$
11) $57x - 36$
12) $67x + 26$

Simplifying Polynomial Expressions

1) $7x^3 - 5x^2 + 15x$
2) $-6x^5 + 10x^4 - 9x^2$
3) $3x^3 - x^2 + 18x$
4) $-5x^4 + 3x^3 + x^2 - 3x$

5) $x^4 - 3x^2 - x$
6) $12x^2 - 4$
7) $12x^4 - 13x^3 - 3x$
8) $-14x^3 - 12x^2 + 18x$

Translate Phrases into an Algebraic Statement

1) $9 - y$
2) $y + 16$
3) 8^2
4) $7x$
5) $y - 22$
6) $\frac{13}{x}$
7) x^5

8) $5 + x$
9) $54 - y$
10) $\frac{11}{x}$
11) $\frac{b^2}{8}$
12) $x - 24 = 18$

The Distributive Property

1) $-4x + 28$
2) $5x - 8$
3) $21x + 49$
4) $9x + 42$
5) $-21x + 18$
6) $42x + 30$

7) $48x + 36$
8) $-15x + 25$
9) $72x - 45$
10) $64x - 8$
11) $48x - 180$
12) $30x - 40$

Evaluating One Variable

1) 3
2) −7
3) 8
4) 7
5) 20
6) 18

7) 17
8) −3
9) 11
10) 228
11) −81
12) 34

Evaluating Two Variables

1) 5
2) 8
3) 17
4) −5
5) 21
6) 21
7) 38

8) 2
9) 39
10) 57
11) 40
12) −71

Combining like Terms

1) $-3x + 5$
2) $-6x + 8$
3) $-26x + 6$
4) $5x - 9$
5) $18x - 22$
6) $19x + 24$

7) $-26x + 15$
8) $10x - 7$
9) $-92x + 15$
10) $11x - 23$
11) $5x + 8$
12) $-43x + 15$

Chapter 8:
Equations and Inequalities

Math Topics that you'll learn in this Chapter:

- ✓ One–Step Equations

- ✓ Multi–Step Equations

- ✓ Graphing Single–Variable Inequalities

- ✓ One–Step Inequalities

- ✓ Multi–Step Inequalities

"Life is a math equation. In order to gain the most, you have to know how to convert negatives into positives."

– Anonymous

One–Step Equations

Step-by-step guide:

✓ The values of two expressions on both sides of an equation are equal. $ax + b = c$

✓ You only need to perform one Math operation in order to solve the one-step equations.

✓ To solve one-step equation, find the inverse (opposite) operation is being performed.

✓ The inverse operations are:
- Addition and subtraction
- Multiplication and division

Examples:

1) **Solve this equation.** $2x = 16, x =?$
Here, the operation is multiplication (variable x is multiplied by 3) and its inverse operation is division. To solve this equation, divide both sides of **equation by** 2:
$$2x = 16 \rightarrow 2x \div 2 = 16 \div 2 \rightarrow x = 8$$

2) **Solve this equation.** $x + 12 = 0, x = ?$
Here, the operation is addition and its inverse operation is subtraction. To solve this equation, subtract 12 from both sides of the **equation:** $x + 12 - 12 = 0 - 12$
Then simplify: $x + 12 - 12 = 0 - 12 \rightarrow x = -12$

 **Solve each equation.**

1) $14 = -2 + x, x = $ ____

2) $x + 7 = 14, x = $ ____

3) $x - 3 = 15, x = $ ____

4) $6 = 14 + x, x = $ ____

5) $x - 4 = 5, x = $ ____

6) $3 - x = -11, x = $ ____

7) $x - 5 = -15, x = $ ____

8) $x - 14 = 14, x = $ ____

9) $x - 15 = -30, x = $ ____

10) $x - 12 = 34, x = $ ____

11) $9 - x = 5, x = $ ____

12) $x - 16 = 16, x = $ ____

Multi–Step Equations

Step-by-step guide:

- ✓ Combine "like" terms on one side.
- ✓ Bring variables to one side by adding or subtracting.
- ✓ Simplify using the inverse of addition or subtraction.
- ✓ Simplify further by using the inverse of multiplication or division.

Examples:

1) **Solve this equation.** $-(8 - x) = 6$

First use Distributive Property: $-(8 - x) = -8 + x$

Now solve by subtract 6 to both sides of the equation. $-8 + x = 6 \rightarrow -8 + x - 6 = 6 - 6$

Now simplify: $-14 + x = 0 \rightarrow x = 14$

2) **Solve this equation.** $2x + 5 = 15 - x$

First bring variables to one side by adding x to both sides.

$2x + 5 = 15 - x \rightarrow 3x + 5 = 15$. Now, subtract 15 from both sides:

$3x + 5 - 15 = 15 - 15 \rightarrow 3x - 10 = 0 \rightarrow 3x = 10$

Now, divide both sides by 3: $3x = 10 \rightarrow 3x \div 3 = \frac{10}{3} \rightarrow x = \frac{10}{3}$

✍ *Solve each equation.*

1) $-(3 - x) = 7$

2) $3x - 15 = 12$

3) $3x - 3 = 9$

4) $3x - 15 = 6$

5) $-3(5 + x) = 3$

6) $-5(3 + x) = 5$

7) $24 = -(x - 7)$

8) $6(4 - 2x) = 30$

9) $18 - 4x = -9 - x$

10) $14 - 2x = 14 + x$

11) $30 + 15x = -6 + 3x$

12) $18 = (-4x) - 9 + 3$

Graphing Single–Variable Inequalities

Step-by-step guide:

✓ Inequality is similar to equations and uses symbols for "less than" (<) and "greater than" (>).
✓ To solve inequalities, we need to isolate the variable. (like in equations)
✓ To graph an inequality, find the value of the inequality on the number line.
✓ For less than or greater than draw open circle on the value of the variable.
✓ If there is an equal sign too, then use filled circle.
✓ Draw a line to the right or to the left for greater or less than.

Examples:

1) **Draw a graph for** $x > 4$

Since, the variable is greater

than 4, then we need to find 4 and draw an open circle above it. Then, draw a line to the right.

2) **Graph this inequality.** $x < 5$

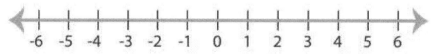

✍ **Draw a graph for each inequality.**

1) $x > 2$

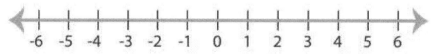

2) $x < -2$

3) $x < 4$

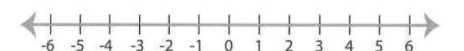

4) $x > -1$

5) $x < 5$

One–Step Inequalities

Step-by-step guide:

✓ Similar to equations, first isolate the variable by using inverse operation.
✓ For dividing or multiplying both sides by negative numbers, flip the direction of the inequality sign.

Examples:

1) **Solve and graph the inequality.** $x + 2 \geq 3$.

Subtract 2 from both sides. $x + 2 \geq 3 \rightarrow x + 2 - 2 \geq 3 - 2$, then: $x \geq 1$

2) **Solve this inequality.** $x - 1 \leq 2$

Add 1 to both sides. $x - 1 \leq 2 \rightarrow x - 1 + 1 \leq 2 + 1$, then: $x \leq 3$

✎ **Solve each inequality and graph it.**

1) $4x \geq 8$

2) $2 + x \leq 6$

3) $x + 4 \leq 9$

4) $8x \geq 24$

5) $5x \leq 20$

Multi–Step Inequalities

Step-by-step guide:

- ✓ Isolate the variable.
- ✓ Simplify using the inverse of addition or subtraction.
- ✓ Simplify further by using the inverse of multiplication or division.

Examples:

1) **Solve this inequality.** $x - 2 \leq 4$

First add 2 to both sides: $x - 2 + 2 \leq 4 + 2 \rightarrow x \leq 6$

2) **Solve this inequality.** $2x + 6 \leq 10$

First add 4 to both sides: $2x + 6 - 6 \leq 10 - 6$

Then simplify: $2x + 6 - 6 \leq 10 - 6 \rightarrow 2x \leq 4$

Now divide both sides by 2: $\frac{2x}{2} \leq \frac{4}{2} \rightarrow x \leq 2$

✍ **Solve each inequality.**

1) $x - 5 \leq 4$

2) $2x - 2 \leq 12$

3) $3 + 2x \leq 11$

4) $x - 6 \geq 12$

5) $3x - 6 \leq 12$

6) $7x - 3 \leq 18$

7) $2x - 3 < 23$

8) $15 - 2x \geq -15$

9) $7 + 3x < 25$

10) $2 + 4x \geq 18$

11) $7 + 3x < 34$

12) $5x - 2 < 8$

Answers – Chapter 8

One–Step Equations

1) 16
2) 7
3) 18
4) −8
5) 9
6) 14

7) −10
8) 28
9) −15
10) 46
11) 4
12) 32

Multi–Step Equations

1) 10
2) 9
3) 4
4) 7
5) −6
6) −4
7) −17

8) $-\frac{1}{2}$
9) 9
10) 0
11) −3
12) −6

Graphing Single–Variable Inequalities

1)

2)

3)

4)

5)

One–Step Inequalities

1)

2)

3)

4)

5)

Multi–Step inequalities

1) $x \leq 9$
2) $x \leq 7$
3) $x \leq 4$
4) $x \geq 18$
5) $x \leq 6$
6) $x \leq 3$
7) $x < 13$
8) $x \leq 15$
9) $x < 6$
10) $x \geq 4$
11) $x < 9$
12) $x < 2$

Chapter 9:
System of Equations

Math Topics that you'll learn in this Chapter:

- ✓ Solving Systems of Equations

- ✓ Systems of Equations Word Problems

Mathematics is a hard thing to love. It has the unfortunate habit, like a rude dog, of turning its most unfavorable side towards you when you first make contact with it. ~ David Whiteland

Systems of Equations

Step-by-step guide:

- ✓ A system of equations contains two equations and two variables. For example, consider the system of equations: $x - y = 1, x + y = 5$
- ✓ The easiest way to solve a system of equation is using the elimination method. The elimination method uses the addition property of equality. You can add the same value to each side of an equation.
- ✓ For the first equation above, you can add $x + y$ to the left side and 5 to the right side of the first equation: $x - y + (x + y) = 1 + 5$. Now, if you simplify, you get: $x - y + (x + y) = 1 + 5 \rightarrow 2x = 6 \rightarrow x = 3$. Now, substitute 3 for the x in the first equation: $3 - y = 1$. By solving this equation, $y = 2$

Example:

What is the value of $x + y$ in this system of equations? $\begin{cases} 2x + 5y = 11 \\ 4x - 2y = -26 \end{cases}$

Solving Systems of Equations by Elimination

Multiply the first equation by (-2), then add it to the second equation.

$$\begin{array}{c} -2(2x + 5y = 11) \\ \underline{4x - 2y = -26} \end{array} \Rightarrow \begin{array}{c} -4x - 10y = -22 \\ 4x - 2y = -26 \end{array} \Rightarrow -12y = -48 \Rightarrow y = 4$$

Plug in the value of y into one of the equations and solve for x.

$2x + 5(4) = 11 \Rightarrow 2x + 20 = 11 \Rightarrow 2x = -9 \Rightarrow x = -4.5$

Thus, $x + y = -4.5 + 4 = -0.5$

✍ **Solve each system of equations.**

1) $-4x - 6y = 7$ $x = $ ____

       $x - 2y = 7$ $y = $ ____

2) $-5x + y = -3$ $x = $ ____

       $3x - 7y = 21$ $y = $ ____

3) $3y = -6x + 12$ $x = $ ____

       $8x - 9y = -10$ $y = $ ____

4) $x + 15y = 50$ $x = $ ____

       $x + 10y = 40$ $y = $ ____

5) $3x - 2y = 15$ $x = $ ____

       $3x - 5y = 15$ $y = $ ____

6) $3x - 6y = -12$ $x = $ ____

       $-x - 3y = -6$ $y = $ ____

Systems of Equations Word Problems

Step-by-step guide:

✓ Define your variables, write two equations, and use elimination method for solving systems of equations.

Example:

Tickets to a movie cost $8 for adults and $5 for students. A group of friends purchased **20** tickets for $115.00. How many adults ticket did they buy? ____

Let x be the number of adult tickets and y be the number of student tickets. There are 20 tickets. Then: $x + y = 20$. The cost of adults' tickets is $8 and for students it is $5, and the total cost is $115. So, $8x + 5y = 115$. Now, we have a system of equations: $\begin{cases} x + y = 20 \\ 8x + 5y = 115 \end{cases}$

Multiply the first equation by -5 and add to the second equation: $-5(x + y = 20) = -5x - 5y = -100$

$8x + 5y + (-5x - 5y) = 115 - 100 \rightarrow 3x = 15 \rightarrow x = 5 \rightarrow 5 + y = 20 \rightarrow y = 15$. There are 5 adult tickets and 15 student tickets.

✎ *Solve each word problem.*

1) A theater is selling tickets for a performance. Mr. Smith purchased 8 senior tickets and 5 child tickets for $136 for his friends and family. Mr. Jackson purchased 4 senior tickets and 6 child tickets for $96. What is the price of a senior ticket? $_____

2) The difference of two numbers is 6. Their sum is 14. What is the bigger number? $_____

3) The sum of the digits of a certain two-digit number is 7. Reversing its digits increase the number by 9. What is the number? _____

4) The difference of two numbers is 18. Their sum is 66. What are the numbers? _____

Answers – Chapter 9

Systems of Equations

1) $x = 2, y = -\frac{5}{2}$
2) $x = 0, y = -3$
3) $x = 1, y = 2$
4) $x = 20, y = 2$
5) $x = 5, y = 0$
6) $x = 0, y = 2$

Systems of Equations Word Problems

1) $12
2) 10
3) 34
4) 42, 24

Chapter 10:
Lines and Slope

Math Topics that you'll learn in this Chapter:

✓ Finding Slope

✓ Graphing Lines Using Slope–Intercept Form

✓ Graphing Lines Using Standard Form

✓ Writing Linear Equations

✓ Graphing Linear Inequalities

✓ Finding Midpoint

✓ Finding Distance of Two Points

"Nature is written in mathematical language." – Galileo Galilei

Finding Slope

Step-by-step guide:

✓ The slope of a line represents the direction of a line on the coordinate plane.
✓ A coordinate plane contains two perpendicular number lines. The horizontal line is x and the vertical line is y. The point at which the two axes intersect is called the origin. An ordered pair (x, y) shows the location of a point.
✓ A line on coordinate plane can be drawn by connecting two points.
✓ To find the slope of a line, we need two points.
✓ The slope of a line with two points A (x_1, y_1) and B (x_2, y_2) can be found by using this formula: $\frac{y_2 - y_1}{x_2 - x_1} = \frac{rise}{run}$

Examples:

1) **Find the slope of the line through these two points:** $(1, -9)$ *and* $(2, 5)$.

Slope $= \frac{y_2 - y_1}{x_2 - x_1}$. Let (x_1, y_1) be $(1, -9)$ and (x_2, y_2) be $(2, 5)$. **Then:** slope $= \frac{y_2 - y_1}{x_2 - x_1} = \frac{5 - (-9)}{2 - 1} = \frac{5+9}{1} = \frac{14}{1} = 14$

2) **Find the slope of the line containing two points** $(6, 1)$ and $(-2, 9)$.

Slope $= \frac{y_2 - y_1}{x_2 - x_1} \rightarrow (x_1, y_1) = (6,1)$ and $(x_2, y_2) = (-2,9)$. **Then:** slope $= \frac{y_2 - y_1}{x_2 - x_1} = \frac{9-1}{-2-6} = \frac{8}{-8} = \frac{1}{-1} = -1$

✎ *Find the slope of the line through each pair of points.*

1) $(7, 4), (5, -2)$

2) $(1, 1), (3, 5)$

3) $(5, 1), (2, 4)$

4) $(-3, 1), (-2, 4)$

5) $(-1, 2), (2, -2)$

6) $(-1, 2), (0, 3)$

7) $(5, -1), (-1, 2)$

8) $(-2, -1), (0, 5)$

9) $(3, 2), (5, 4)$

10) $(5, -4), (2, -1)$

11) $(2, -9), (1, -8)$

12) $(7, -2), (5, 0)$

Graphing Lines Using Slope–Intercept Form

Step-by-step guide:

✓ Slope-intercept form of a line: given the slope m and the y-intercept (the intersection of the line and y-axis) b, then the equation of the line is:
$$y = mx + b$$

Example: Sketch the graph of $y = 6x - 1$.

To graph this line, we need to find two points. When x *is zero the value of* y *is* -1*. And when* y *is zero the value of* x *is* $\frac{1}{6}$*.* x $= 0 \rightarrow$ y $= 6(0) - 1 = -1$, y $= 0 \rightarrow 0 = 6$x $- 1 \rightarrow$ x $= \frac{1}{6}$

Now, we have two points: (0,-1*) and (*$\frac{1}{6}$*,0). Find the points and graph the line. Remember that the slope of the line is* 6*.*

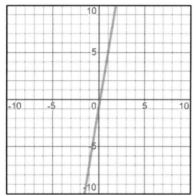

✎ *Sketch the graph of each line.*

1) $y = x + 4$

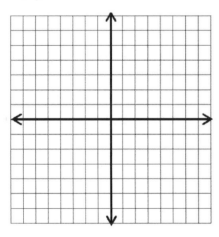

2) $y = 2x - 1$

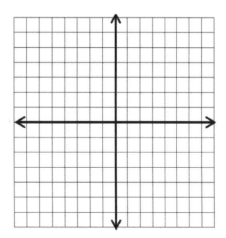

Graphing Lines Using Standard Form

Step-by-step guide:

- ✓ Find the x –intercept of the line by putting zero for y.
- ✓ Find the y –intercept of the line by putting zero for the x.
- ✓ Connect these two points.

Example:

Sketch the graph of $x - y = -2$.

First isolate y for x: $x - y = -2 \rightarrow y = x + 2$

Find the x–intercept of the line by putting zero for y.

$y = x + 2 \rightarrow x + 2 = 0 \rightarrow x = -2$

Find the y–intercept of the line by putting zero for the x.

$y = 0 + 2 \rightarrow y = 2$

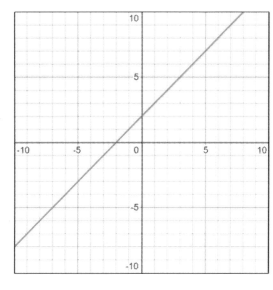

Then: x–intercept: $(-2,0)$ and y–intercept: $(0,2)$

✎ ***Sketch the graph of each line.***

1) $y = -x - 2$ 2) $y = x + 3$ 3) $x + y = -1$

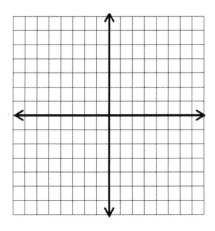 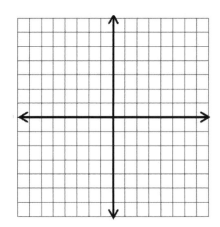 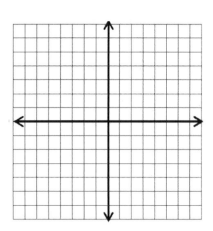

Writing Linear Equations

Step-by-step guide:

✓ The equation of a line: $y = mx + b$

✓ Identify the slope.

✓ Find the y-intercept. This can be done by substituting the slope and the coordinates of a point (x, y) on the line.

Example:

1) What is the equation of the line that passes through $(1, -2)$ and has a slope of 6?

The general slope-intercept form of the equation of a line is $y = mx + b$, where m is the slope and b is the y-intercept.

By substitution of the given point and given slope, we have: $-2 = (1)(6) + b$

So, $b = -2 - 6 = -8$, and the required equation is $y = 6x - 8$.

2) Write the equation of the line through $(1, 1)$ and $(-1, 3)$.

$Slop = \frac{y_2 - y_1}{x_2 - x_1} = \frac{3-1}{-1-1} = \frac{2}{-2} = -1 \rightarrow m = -1$

To find the value of b, you can use either points. The answer will be the same: $y = -x + b$

$(1, 1) \rightarrow 1 = -1 + b \rightarrow b = 2$

$(-1, 3) \rightarrow 3 = -(-1) + b \rightarrow b = 2$

The equation of the line is: $y = -x + 2$

✍ *Write the equation of the line through the given points.*

1) through: $(2, 4), (1, 2)$

2) through: $(-3, 1), (1, 5)$

3) through: $(-2, 1), (1, 7)$

4) through: $(4, 3), (2, 1)$

5) through: $(-4, 5), (-3, 2)$

6) through: $(8, 3), (7, 2)$

7) through: $(3, -3), (1, 5)$

8) through: $(1, 7), (-4, -3)$

Graphing Linear Inequalities

Step-by-step guide:

- ✓ First, graph the "equals" line.
- ✓ Choose a testing point. (it can be any point on both sides of the line.)
- ✓ Put the value of (x, y) of that point in the inequality. If that works, that part of the line is the solution. If the values don't work, then the other part of the line is the solution.

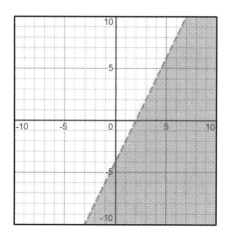

Example:

Sketch the graph of $y < 2x - 4$. First, graph the line:

$y = 2x - 4$. The slope is 2 and y-intercept is -4. Then, choose a testing point. The easiest point to test is the origin: $(0, 0)$

$$(0,0) \rightarrow y < 2x - 4 \rightarrow 0 < 2(0) - 4 \rightarrow 0 < -4$$

0 is not less than -4. So, the other part of the line (on the right side) is the solution.

✎ *Sketch the graph of each linear inequality.*

1) $y > 2x - 1$ **2)** $y < -2x + 1$ **3)** $y \leq -3x + 4$

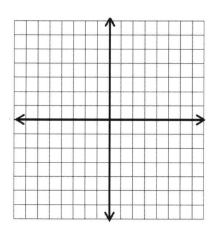 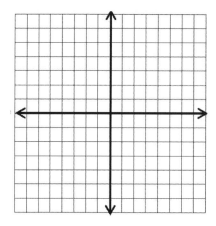 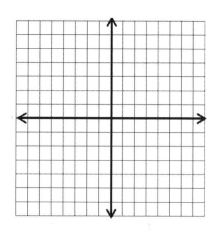

Finding Midpoint

Step-by-step guide:

- ✓ The middle of a line segment is its midpoint.
- ✓ The Midpoint of two endpoints A (x_1, y_1) and B (x_2, y_2) can be found using this formula: M $(\frac{x_1+x_2}{2}, \frac{y_1+y_2}{2})$

Example:

1) Find the midpoint of the line segment with the given endpoints. $(1, -2), (3, 6)$

Midpoint $= (\frac{x_1+x_2}{2}, \frac{y_1+y_2}{2}) \rightarrow (x_1, y_1) = (1, -2)$ and $(x_2, y_2) = (3, 6)$

Midpoint $= (\frac{1+3}{2}, \frac{-2+6}{2}) \rightarrow (\frac{4}{2}, \frac{4}{2}) \rightarrow M(2, 2)$

2) Find the midpoint of the line segment with the given endpoints. $(-2, 5), (8, -3)$

Midpoint $= (\frac{x_1+x_2}{2}, \frac{y_1+y_2}{2}) \rightarrow (x_1, y_1) = (-2, 5)$ and $(x_2, y_2) = (8, -3)$

Midpoint $= (\frac{-2+8}{2}, \frac{5-3}{2}) \rightarrow (\frac{6}{2}, \frac{2}{2}) \rightarrow M(3, 1)$

✍ *Find the midpoint of the line segment with the given endpoints.*

1) $(2, -1), (0, 3)$

2) $(6, 1), (-2, 5)$

3) $(4, -1), (0, 3)$

4) $(3, 7), (-1, 3)$

5) $(-3, 2), (9, -6)$

6) $(-2, 3), (2, -3)$

7) $(8, 0), (-6, 4)$

8) $(-1, 4), (-3, 0)$

9) $(4, 7), (-2, 5)$

10) $(9, 3), (-3, -7)$

11) $(3, 4), (-9, -6)$

12) $(-2, 8), (-6, -2)$

Finding Distance of Two Points

Step-by-step guide:

✓ Distance of two points A (x_1, y_1) and B (x_2, y_2): $d = \sqrt{(x_2 - x_1)^2 + (y_2 - y_1)^2}$

Example:

1) Find the distance between of $(1, 6), (4, 2)$.

   Use distance of two points formula: $d = \sqrt{(x_2 - x_1)^2 + (y_2 - y_1)^2}$

   $(x_1, y_1) = (1, 6)$ and $(x_2, y_2) = (4, 2)$. ***Then:*** $d = \sqrt{(x_2 - x_1)^2 + (y_2 - y_1)^2} \rightarrow$

   $d = \sqrt{(4 - (1))^2 + (2 - 6)^2} = \sqrt{(3)^2 + (-4)^2} = \sqrt{9 + 16} = \sqrt{25} = 5 \rightarrow d = 5$

2) Find the distance of two points $(-1, 5)$ ***and*** $(-3, -6)$.

   Use distance of two points formula: $d = \sqrt{(x_2 - x_1)^2 + (y_2 - y_1)^2}$

   $(x_1, y_1) = (-1, 5)$, and $(x_2, y_2) = (-3, -6)$

   Then: $d = \sqrt{(x_2 - x_1)^2 + (y_2 - y_1)^2} \rightarrow d = \sqrt{(-3 - (-1))^2 + (-6 - (5))^2} =$

   $\sqrt{(-2)^2 + (-11)^2} = \sqrt{4 + 121} = \sqrt{125} = 5\sqrt{5}$. Then: $d = 5\sqrt{5}$

✎ ***Find the distance between each pair of points.***

1) $(-6, 0), (-2, 3)$

2) $(4, 2), (-2, -6)$

3) $(-4, -2), (4, 4)$

4) $(-6, -10), (-2, -10)$

5) $(-1, 1), (-6, -7)$

6) $(3, 2), (8, 2)$

7) $(8, 4), (3, -8)$

8) $(4, 4), (12, 19)$

9) $(-5, 10), (7, 1)$

10) $(7, 7), (-9, -5)$

11) $(9, -3), (3, -11)$

12) $(1, 0), (6, 12)$

Answers – Chapter 10

Finding Slope

1) 3
2) 2
3) -1
4) 3
5) $-\frac{4}{3}$
6) 1

7) $-\frac{1}{2}$
8) 3
9) 1
10) -1
11) -1
12) -1

Graphing Lines Using Slope–Intercept Form

1)

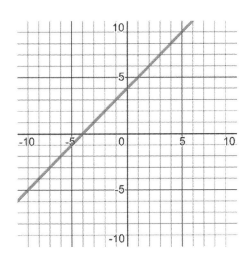

2)

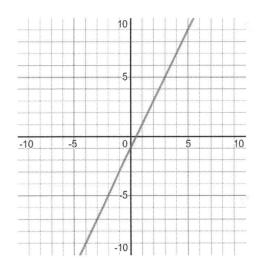

Graphing Lines Using Standard Form

1)

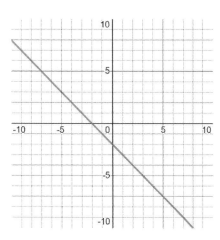

2)

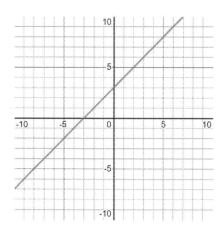

3)

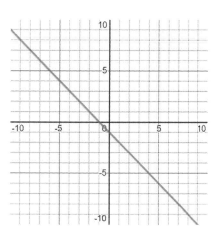

Writing Linear Equations

1) $y = 2x$
2) $y = x + 4$
3) $y = 2x + 5$
4) $y = x - 1$

5) $y = -3x - 7$
6) $y = x - 5$
7) $y = -4x + 9$
8) $y = 2x + 5$

Graphing Linear Inequalities

1)

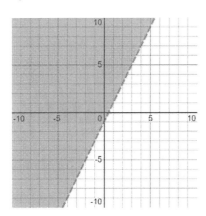

2)

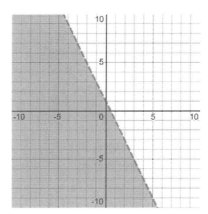

3)

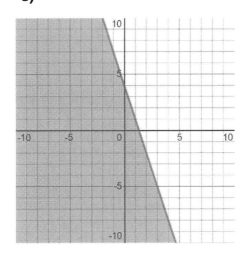

Finding Midpoint

1) $(1, 1)$
2) $(2, 3)$
3) $(2, 1)$
4) $(1, 5)$

5) $(3, -2)$
6) $(0, 0)$
7) $(1, 2)$
8) $(-2, 2)$

9) $(1, 6)$
10) $(3, -2)$
11) $(-3, -1)$
12) $(-4, 3)$

Finding Distance of Two Points

1) 5
2) 10
3) 10
4) 4

5) 9.4
6) 5
7) 13
8) 17

9) 15
10) 20
11) 10
12) 13

Chapter 11:
Exponents and Variables

Math Topics that you'll learn in this Chapter:

- ✓ Multiplication Property of Exponents

- ✓ Division Property of Exponents

- ✓ Powers of Products and Quotients

- ✓ Zero and Negative Exponents

- ✓ Negative Exponents and Negative Bases

- ✓ Scientific Notation

- ✓ Square Roots

Mathematics is an art of human understanding. ~ William Thurston

Multiplication Property of Exponents

Step-by-step guide:

- ✓ Exponents are shorthand for repeated multiplication of the same number by itself. For example, instead of 2×2, we can write 2^2. For $3 \times 3 \times 3 \times 3$, we can write 3^4
- ✓ In algebra, a variable is a letter used to stand for a number. The most common letters are: $x, y, z, a, b, c, m,$ and n.
- ✓ Exponent's rules: $x^a \times x^b = x^{a+b}$, $\frac{x^a}{x^b} = x^{a-b}$

$$(x^a)^b = x^{a \times b}, \qquad (xy)^a = x^a \times y^a , \left(\frac{a}{b}\right)^c = \frac{a^c}{b^c}$$

Examples:

1) **Multiply.** $4x^3 \times 2x^2 =$

Use Exponent's rules: $x^a \times x^b = x^{a+b} \rightarrow x^3 \times x^2 = x^{3+2} = x^5$

Then: $4x^3 \times 2x^2 = 8x^5$

2) **Multiply.** $(x^3y^5)^2 =$

Use Exponent's rules: $(x^a)^b = x^{a \times b}$. Then: $(x^3y^5)^2 = x^{3 \times 2}y^{5 \times 2} = x^6y^{10}$

✎ *Simplify and write the answer in exponential form.*

1) $2x^2 \times 4x =$

2) $5x^4 \times x^2 =$

3) $8x^4 \times 3x^5 =$

4) $3x^2 \times 6xy =$

5) $2x^5y \times 4x^2y^3 =$

6) $9x^2y^5 \times 5x^2y^8 =$

7) $5x^2y \times 5x^2y^7 =$

8) $7x^6 \times 3x^9y^4 =$

9) $8x^8y^5 \times 7x^5y^3 =$

10) $9x^6x^2 \times 4xy^5 =$

11) $12xy^7 \times 2x^9y^8 =$

12) $9x^9y^{12} \times 9x^{14}y^{11} =$

Division Property of Exponents

Step-by-step guide:

✓ For division of exponents use these formulas: $\frac{x^a}{x^b} = x^{a-b}$, $x \neq 0$

$$\frac{x^a}{x^b} = \frac{1}{x^{b-a}} , x \neq 0, \qquad \frac{1}{x^b} = x^{-b}$$

Examples:

1) **Simplify.** $\frac{12\,^2y}{4xy^3} =$

First cancel the common factor: $4 \rightarrow \frac{12x^2y}{4xy^3} = \frac{3x^2y}{xy^3}$

Use Exponent's rules: $\frac{x^a}{x^b} = x^{a-b} \rightarrow \frac{x^2}{x} = x^{2-1} = x$ and $\frac{y}{y^3} = y^{1-3} = y^{-2}$

Then: $\frac{12x^2y}{4xy^3} = \frac{3x}{y^2}$

2) **Divide.** $\frac{18\,^{-6}}{2x^{-3}} =$

Use Exponent's rules: $\frac{x^a}{x^b} = \frac{1}{x^{b-a}} \rightarrow \frac{x^{-6}}{x^{-3}} = \frac{1}{x^{-3-(-6)}} = \frac{1}{x^{-3+6}} = \frac{1}{x^3}$

Then: $\frac{18x^{-6}}{2x^{-3}} = \frac{9}{x^3}$

✍ **Simplify.**

1) $\frac{5^2 \times 5^3}{5^4 \times 5^2} =$

2) $\frac{4x}{8x^2} =$

3) $\frac{15x^6}{3x^5} =$

4) $\frac{18\,^5}{12x^8} =$

5) $\frac{24x^5}{4y^3} =$

6) $\frac{36xy^3}{2x^5y^2} =$

7) $\frac{8x^8y}{3xy^2} =$

8) $\frac{20x^5y^9}{4x^3} =$

9) $\frac{28\,^2}{8x^5y^3} =$

10) $\frac{25yx^4}{5yx^8} =$

11) $\frac{45\,^4y}{9x^8y^2} =$

12) $\frac{4x^8y^2}{20\,^8y} =$

Powers of Products and Quotients

Step-by-step guide:

✓ For any nonzero numbers a and b and any integer x, $(ab)^x = a^x \times b^x$.

Example:

1) ***Simplify.*** $(6x^2y^4)^2 =$

Use Exponent's rules: $(x^a)^b = x^{a \times b}$

$(6x^2y^4)^2 = (6)^2(x^2)^2(y^4)^2 = 36x^{2 \times 2}y^{4 \times 2} = 36x^4y^8$

2) ***Simplify.*** $(\frac{5x}{2x^2})^2 =$

First cancel the common factor: $x \rightarrow (\frac{5x}{2x^2})^2 = (\frac{5}{2x})^2$

Use Exponent's rules: $(\frac{a}{b})^c = \frac{a^c}{b^c}$

Then: $(\frac{5}{2x})^2 = \frac{5^2}{(2x)^2} = \frac{25}{4x^2}$

✎ ***Simplify.***

1) $(x^2y^6)^2 =$

2) $(x^3 \times y)^2 =$

3) $(2x^5y^3)^2 =$

4) $(3x^3y^6)^2 =$

5) $(4x^5y^6)^3 =$

6) $(5x \times 2y^5)^2 =$

7) $(\frac{3x}{x^2})^3 =$

8) $\left(\frac{x^2y^3}{x^2y^2}\right)^3 =$

9) $\left(\frac{16x}{4x^6}\right)^2 =$

10) $\left(\frac{2x^5}{x^2y^2}\right)^2 =$

11) $\left(\frac{xy^2}{x^2y^3}\right)^{-2} =$

12) $\left(\frac{8xy^2}{x^3}\right)^2 =$

Zero and Negative Exponents

Step-by-step guide:

✓ A negative exponent simply means that the base is on the wrong side of the fraction line, so you need to flip the base to the other side. For instance, "x^{-2}" (pronounced as "ecks to the minus two") just means "x^2" but underneath, as in $\frac{1}{x^2}$.

Example:

1) **Evaluate.** $\left(\frac{2}{3}\right)^{-2} =$

Use Exponent's rules: $\frac{1}{x^b} = x^{-b} \rightarrow \left(\frac{2}{3}\right)^{-2} = \frac{1}{\left(\frac{2}{3}\right)^2} = \frac{1}{\frac{2^2}{3^2}}$

Now use fraction rule: $\frac{1}{\frac{b}{c}} = \frac{c}{b} \rightarrow \frac{1}{\frac{2^2}{3^2}} = \frac{3^2}{2^2} = \frac{9}{4}$

2) **Evaluate.** $\left(\frac{4}{5}\right)^{-3} =$

Use Exponent's rules: $\frac{1}{x^b} = x^{-b} \rightarrow \left(\frac{4}{5}\right)^{-3} = \frac{1}{\left(\frac{4}{5}\right)^3} = \frac{1}{\frac{4^3}{5^3}}$

Now use fraction rule: $\frac{1}{\frac{b}{c}} = \frac{c}{b} \rightarrow \frac{1}{\frac{4^3}{5^3}} = \frac{5^3}{4^3} = \frac{125}{64}$

✍ *Evaluate the following expressions.*

1) $3^{-2} =$

2) $2^{-3} =$

3) $5^{-3} =$

4) $4^{-3} =$

5) $6^{-3} =$

6) $8^{-2} =$

7) $5^{-4} =$

8) $10^{-2} =$

9) $\left(\frac{1}{5}\right)^{-1}$

10) $\left(\frac{1}{4}\right)^{-2} =$

11) $\left(\frac{1}{5}\right)^{-3} =$

12) $\left(\frac{3}{4}\right)^{-2} =$

Negative Exponents and Negative Bases

Step-by-step guide:

- ✓ Make the power positive. A negative exponent is the reciprocal of that number with a positive exponent.
- ✓ The parenthesis is important!
- ✓ 5^{-2} is not the same as $(-5)^{-2}$

$$(-5)^{-2} = -\frac{1}{5^2} \text{ and } (-5)^{-2} = +\frac{1}{5^2}$$

Example:

1) **Simplify.** $\left(\frac{5a}{6c}\right)^{-2} =$

Use Exponent's rules: $\frac{1}{x^b} = x^{-b} \rightarrow \left(\frac{5a}{6c}\right)^{-2} = \frac{1}{\left(\frac{5a}{6c}\right)^2} = \frac{1}{\frac{5^2a^2}{6^2c^2}}$

Now use fraction rule: $\frac{1}{\frac{b}{c}} = \frac{c}{b} \rightarrow \frac{1}{\frac{5^2a^2}{6^2c^2}} = \frac{6^2c^2}{5^2a^2}$

Then: $\frac{6^2c^2}{5^2a^2} = \frac{36c^2}{25\,^2}$

2) **Simplify.** $\left(\frac{2x}{3yz}\right)^{-3} =$

Use Exponent's rules: $\frac{1}{x^b} = x^{-b} \rightarrow \left(\frac{2x}{3yz}\right)^{-3} = \frac{1}{\left(\frac{2x}{3y}\right)^3} = \frac{1}{\frac{2^3x^3}{3^3y^3z^3}}$

Now use fraction rule: $\frac{1}{\frac{b}{c}} = \frac{c}{b} \rightarrow \frac{1}{\frac{2^3x^3}{3^3y^3z^3}} = \frac{3^3y^3z^3}{2^3x^3} = \frac{27y^3z^3}{8x^3}$

✎ **Simplify.**

1) $2x^{-2}y^{-3} =$

2) $3x^{-5}y^{-2} =$

3) $6a^{-3}b^{-5} =$

4) $7x^4y^{-3} =$

5) $-\frac{9}{x^{-4}} =$

6) $\frac{12b}{-9c^{-5}} =$

7) $\frac{16ab}{a^{-2}b^{-3}} =$

8) $\frac{15n^{-2}}{20\,^{-3}} =$

9) $\frac{16ab^{-5}}{4c^{-2}} =$

10) $\left(\frac{5x}{2y}\right)^{-2} =$

11) $\left(-\frac{2x}{3yz}\right)^{-4} =$

12) $\frac{5ab^{-3}}{-3c^{-2}} =$

13) $\left(-\frac{x^5}{x^3}\right)^{-2} =$

Scientific Notation

Step-by-step guide:

✓ It is used to write very big or very small numbers in decimal form.
✓ In scientific notation all numbers are written in the form of:

$$m \times 10^n$$

Decimal notation	Scientific notation
5	5×10^0
− 25,000	-2.5×10^4
0.5	5×10^{-1}
2,122.456	$2,122456 \times 10^{-3}$

Example:

1) *Write* 0.00015 *in scientific notation.*

First, move the decimal point to the right so that you have a number that is between 1 and 10. Then: $N = 1.5$
Second, determine how many places the decimal moved in step 1 by the power of 10.
Then: $10^{-4} \rightarrow$ When the decimal moved to the right, the exponent is negative.
Then: $0.00015 = 1.5 \times 10^{-4}$

2) *Write* 9.5×10^{-5} *in standard notation.*

$10^{-5} \rightarrow$ When the decimal moved to the right, the exponent is negative.
Then: $9.5 \times 10^{-5} = 0.000095$

 *Write each number in scientific notation.*

1) $15,000,000 =$ 3) $0.000819 =$

2) $67,000 =$ 4) $0.00092 =$

Write each number in standard notation.

5) $4.5 \times 10^3 =$ 7) $6 \times 10^{-1} =$

6) $8 \times 10^{-4} =$ 8) $9 \times 10^{-2} =$

Square Roots

Step-by-step guide:

 ✓ A square root of x is a number r whose square is: $r^2 = x$

  r is a square root of x.

Example:

1) **Find the square root of $\sqrt{169}$.**

 First factor the number: $169 = 13^2$, Then: $\sqrt{169} = \sqrt{13^2}$

 Now use radical rule: $\sqrt[n]{a^n} = a$

 Then: $\sqrt{13^2} = 13$

2) **Evaluate. $\sqrt{9} \times \sqrt{25} =$**

 First factor the numbers: $9 = 3^2$ and $25 = 5^2$

 Then: $\sqrt{9} \times \sqrt{25} = \sqrt{3^2} \times \sqrt{5^2}$

 Now use radical rule: $\sqrt[n]{a^n} = a$, Then: $\sqrt{3^2} \times \sqrt{5^2} = 3 \times 5 = 15$

✎ *Evaluate.*

1) $\sqrt{16} \times \sqrt{4} =$ _____

2) $\sqrt{9} \times \sqrt{49} =$ _____

3) $\sqrt{4} \times \sqrt{8} =$ _____

4) $\sqrt{9} \times \sqrt{6} =$ _____

5) $\sqrt{25} \times \sqrt{5} =$ _____

6) $\sqrt{6} \times \sqrt{6} =$ _____

7) $\sqrt{5} + \sqrt{5} =$ _____

8) $\sqrt{12} + \sqrt{12} =$ _____

9) $3\sqrt{6} - 2\sqrt{6} =$ _____

10) $3\sqrt{5} \times 2\sqrt{5} =$ _____

11) $6\sqrt{8} \times 2\sqrt{8} =$ _____

12) $6\sqrt{4} - \sqrt{16} =$ _____

Answers – Chapter 11

Multiplication Property of Exponents

1) $8x^3$
2) $5x^6$
3) $24x^9$
4) $18x^3y$

5) $8x^7y^4$
6) $45x^4y^{13}$
7) $25x^4y^8$
8) $21x^{15}y^4$

9) $56x^{13}y^8$
10) $36x^9y^5$
11) $24x^{10}y^{15}$
12) $81x^{23}y^{23}$

Division Property of Exponents

1) $\dfrac{1}{5}$
2) $\dfrac{1}{2x}$
3) $5x$
4) $\dfrac{3}{2x^3}$

5) $\dfrac{6x^5}{y^3}$
6) $\dfrac{18y}{x^4}$
7) $\dfrac{8x^7}{3y}$
8) $5x^2y^9$

9) $\dfrac{7}{2x^3y^3}$
10) $\dfrac{5}{x^4}$
11) $\dfrac{5}{x^4y}$
12) $\dfrac{y}{5}$

Powers of Products and Quotients

1) x^4y^{12}
2) x^6y^2
3) $4x^{10}y^6$
4) $9x^6y^{12}$
5) $64x^{15}y^{18}$

6) $100x^2y^{10}$
7) $\dfrac{27}{x^3}$
8) y^3
9) $\dfrac{16}{x^{10}}$

10) $\dfrac{4x^6}{y^4}$
11) x^2y^2
12) $\dfrac{64y^{10}}{x^4}$

Zero and Negative Exponents

1) $\dfrac{1}{9}$
2) $\dfrac{1}{8}$
3) $\dfrac{1}{125}$
4) $\dfrac{1}{64}$

5) $\dfrac{1}{216}$
6) $\dfrac{1}{64}$
7) $\dfrac{1}{625}$
8) $\dfrac{1}{100}$

9) 5
10) 16
11) 125
12) $\dfrac{16}{9}$

Negative Exponents and Negative Bases

1) $\dfrac{2}{x^2 y^3}$

2) $\dfrac{3}{x^5 y^2}$

3) $\dfrac{6}{a^3 b^5}$

4) $\dfrac{7x^4}{y^3}$

5) $-9x^4$

6) $-\dfrac{4bc^5}{3}$

7) $16a^3 b^4$

8) $\dfrac{3p^3}{4n^2}$

9) $\dfrac{4ac^2}{b^5}$

10) $\dfrac{4y^2}{25\ ^2}$

11) $\dfrac{81y^4 z^4}{16x^4}$

12) $-\dfrac{5ac^2}{3b^3}$

13) $\dfrac{1}{x^4}$

Scientific Notation

1) 1.5×10^7

2) 6.7×10^4

3) 8.19×10^{-4}

4) 9.2×10^{-4}

5) $4,500$

6) 0.0008

7) 0.6

8) 0.09

Square Roots

1) 8

2) 21

3) $4\sqrt{2}$

4) $3\sqrt{6}$

5) $5\sqrt{5}$

6) 6

7) $2\sqrt{5}$

8) $4\sqrt{3}$

9) $\sqrt{6}$

10) 30

11) 96

12) 8

Chapter 12:
Polynomials

Math Topics that you'll learn in this Chapter:

- ✓ Writing Polynomials in Standard Form

- ✓ Simplifying Polynomials

- ✓ Adding and Subtracting Polynomials

- ✓ Multiplying Monomials

- ✓ Multiplying and Dividing Monomials

- ✓ Multiplying a Polynomial and a Monomial

- ✓ Multiplying Binomials

- ✓ Factoring Trinomials

- ✓ Operations with Polynomials

Mathematics is the supreme judge; from its decisions there is no appeal. -Tobias Dantzig

Writing Polynomials in Standard Form

Step-by-step guide:

- ✓ A polynomial function $f(x)$ of degree n is of the form
$$f(x) = a_n x^n + a_{n-1} x_{n-1} + \cdots + a_1 x + a_0$$
- ✓ The first term is the one with the biggest power!

Example:

1) Write this polynomial in standard form. $8 + 5x^2 - 3x^3 =$

   The first term is the one with the biggest power: $8 + 5x^2 - 3x^3 = -3x^3 + 5x^2 + 8$

2) Write this polynomial in standard form. $5x^2 - 9x^5 + 8x^3 - 11 =$

   The first term is the one with the biggest power: $5x^2 - 9x^5 + 8x^3 - 11 =$
   $-9x^5 + 8x^3 + 5x^2 - 11$

✍ *Write each polynomial in standard form.*

1) $2x - 5x =$

2) $5 + 12x - 8x =$

3) $x^2 - 2x^3 + 1 =$

4) $2 + 2x^2 - 1 =$

5) $-x^2 + 4x - 2x^3 =$

6) $-2x^2 + 2x^3 + 12 =$

7) $18 - 5x + 9x^4 =$

8) $2x^2 + 13x - 2x^3 =$

9) $8 + 4x^2 - x^3 =$

10) $2x + 3x^3 - 2x^2 =$

11) $-4x^2 + 4x - 6x^3 =$

12) $-3x^2 + 2 - 5x =$

Simplifying Polynomials

Step-by-step guide:

✓ Find "like" terms. (they have same variables with same power).

✓ Use "FOIL". (First–Out–In–Last) for binomials:

$$(x + a)(x + b) = x^2 + (b + a)x + ab$$

✓ Add or Subtract "like" terms using order of operation.

Example:

1) Simplify this expression. $2x(2x - 4) =$

   Use Distributive Property: $2x(2x - 4) = 4x^2 - 8x$

2) Simplify this expression. $(x + 2)(x - 5) =$

   First apply FOIL method: $(a + b)(c + d) = ac + ad + bc + bd$

   $(x + 2)(x - 5) = x^2 - 5x + 2x - 10$

   Now combine like terms: $x^2 - 5x + 2x - 10 = x^2 - 3x - 10$

✍ *Simplify each expression.*

1) $2(4x - 6) =$

2) $5(3x - 4) =$

3) $x(2x - 5) =$

4) $4(5x + 3) =$

5) $2x(6x - 2) =$

6) $x(3x + 8) =$

7) $(x - 2)(x + 4) =$

8) $(x + 3)(x + 2) =$

9) $(x - 4)(x - 7) =$

10) $(2x + 4)(2x - 5) =$

11) $(4x - 3)(x - 6) =$

12) $(3x + 5)(2x + 4) =$

Adding and Subtracting Polynomials

Step-by-step guide:

✓ Adding polynomials is just a matter of combining like terms, with some order of operations considerations thrown in.

✓ Be careful with the minus signs, and don't confuse addition and multiplication!

Example:

1) **Simplify the expressions.** $(2x^3 - 4x^4) - (2x^4 - 6x^3) =$

First use Distributive Property for $-(2x^4 - 6x^3) = -2x^4 + 6x^3$

$(2x^3 - 4x^4) - (2x^4 - 6x^3) = 2x^3 - 4x^4 - 2x^4 + 6x^3$

Now combine like terms: $2x^3 - 4x^4 - 2x^4 + 6x^3 = -6x^4 + 8x^3$

2) **Add expressions.** $(x^3 - 2) + (5x^3 - 3x^2) =$

Remove parentheses: $(x^3 - 2) + (5x^3 - 3x^2) = x^3 - 2 + 5x^3 - 3x^2$

Now combine like terms: $x^3 - 2 + 5x^3 - 3x^2 = 6x^3 - 3x^2 - 2$

✎ *Add or subtract expressions.*

1) $(x^2 - x) + (3x^2 - 5x) =$

2) $(x^3 + 2x) - (3x^3 + 2) =$

3) $(2x^3 - 4) + (2x^3 - 2) =$

4) $(-x^2 - 2) + (2x^2 + 1) =$

5) $(4x^2 + 3) - (3 - 3x^2) =$

6) $(x^3 + 3x^2) - (x^3 - 8) =$

7) $(7x - 9) + (3x + 5) =$

8) $(x^4 - 2x) - (x - x^4) =$

9) $(2x - 4x^3) - (2x^3 + 3x) =$

10) $(x^3 + 5) - (5 - 2x^3) =$

11) $(3x^2 + 2x^3) - (4x^3 + 5) =$

12) $(6x^2 - x) + (2x - 5x^2) =$

Multiplying Monomials

Step-by-step guide:

✓ A monomial is a polynomial with just one term, like $2x$ or $7y$.

Example:

1) **Multiply expressions.** $-2xy^4z^2 \times 4x^2y^5z^3 =$

Use this formula: $x^a \times x^b = x^{a+b}$

$x \times x^2 = x^{1+2} = x^3$, $y^4 \times y^5 = y^{4+5} = y^9$ and $z^2 \times z^3 = z^{2+3} = z^5$

Then: $-2xy^4z^2 \times 4x^2y^5z^3 = -8x^3y^9z^5$

2) **Multiply expressions.** $-4a^4b^3 \times 5a^3b^2 =$

Use this formula: $x^a \times x^b = x^{a+b}$

$a^4 \times a^3 = a^{4+3} = a^7$ and $b^3 \times b^2 = b^{3+2} = b^5$

Then: $-4a^4b^3 \times 5a^3b^2 = -20a^7b^5$

✍ *Simplify each expression.*

1) $(-2x^4) \times (-5x^3) =$

2) $8x^8 \times -2x^2 =$

3) $5xy^4 \times 2x^2 =$

4) $-2x^6y \times 8xy =$

5) $3x^5 \times (-4x^3y^5) =$

6) $9x^3y^2 \times 3x^2y =$

7) $7xy^4 \times 8x^3y^5 =$

8) $(-5x^2y^4) \times (-2xy^3) =$

9) $9x^5y^2 \times 5x^6y^3 =$

10) $12x^5y^2 \times 2x^3y^3 =$

11) $11x^4y^3z \times 3x^5z^2 =$

12) $20x^5y^8 \times 3x^2y^4 =$

Multiplying and Dividing Monomials

Step-by-step guide:

- ✓ When you divide two monomials you need to divide their coefficients and then divide their variables.
- ✓ In case of exponents with the same base, you need to subtract their powers.
- ✓ Exponent's rules:

$$x^a \times x^b = x^{a+b}, \qquad \frac{x^a}{x^b} = x^{a-b}$$

$$\frac{1}{x^b} = x^{-b}, \quad (x^a)^b = x^{a \times b}$$

$$(xy)^a = x^a \times y^a$$

Example:

1) **Multiply expressions.** $(8x^5)(-2x^4) =$
   Use this formula: $x^a \times x^b = x^{a+b} \rightarrow x^5 \times x^4 = x^9$
   Then: $(8x^5)(-2x^4) = -16x^9$

2) **Dividing expressions.** $\frac{-12x^4y^3}{2xy^2} =$
   Use this formula: $\frac{x^a}{x^b} = x^{a-b}$, $\frac{x^4}{x} = x^{4-1} = x^3$ and $\frac{y^3}{y^2} = y$
   Then: $\frac{-12x^4y^3}{2xy^2} = -6x^3y$

✎ *Simplify each expression.*

1) $(x^2y)(xy^2) =$

2) $(x^4y^2)(2x^5y) =$

3) $(-2x^2y)(4x^4y^3) =$

4) $(-3x^5y^2)(2x^2y^4) =$

5) $(-4x^5y^3)(-2x^3y^4) =$

6) $(6x^6y^5)(3x^3y^8) =$

7) $\frac{-2x^4y^3}{x^2y^2} =$

8) $\frac{8x^4y^7}{2x^3y^4} =$

9) $\frac{25\ ^6y^5}{5x^3y^2} =$

10) $\frac{18\ ^{12}y^{14}}{6x^8y^6} =$

11) $\frac{45x^{13}y^{15}}{9x^9y^4} =$

12) $\frac{-60x^{20}y^{16}}{3x^{11}y^{13}} =$

Multiplying a Polynomial and a Monomial

Step-by-step guide:

✓ When multiplying monomials, use the product rule for exponents.

✓ When multiplying a monomial by a polynomial, use the distributive property.

$$a \times (b + c) = a \times b + a \times c$$

Example:

1) **Multiply expressions.** $2x(-2x + 4) =$

Use Distributive Property: $2x(-2x + 4) = -4x^2 + 8x$

2) **Multiply expressions.** $-2x(3x^2 + 4y^2) =$

Use Distributive Property: $-2x(3x^2 + 4y^2) = -6x^3 - 8xy^2$

✍ *Find each product.*

1) $-2x(5x + 2y) =$

2) $3x(2x - y) =$

3) $4x(x + 5y) =$

4) $-4x(6x - 3) =$

5) $x(-2x + 9y) =$

6) $2x(5x - 8y) =$

7) $x(2x + 4y - 3) =$

8) $2x(x^2 - 2y^2) =$

9) $-4x(2x + 4y) =$

10) $3(x^2 + 7y^2) =$

11) $4x(-x^2y + 2y) =$

12) $5(x^2 - 4xy + 6) =$

Multiplying Binomials

Step-by-step guide:

✓ Use "FOIL". (First-Out-In-Last)
$$(x + a)(x + b) = x^2 + (b + a)x + ab$$

Example:

1) **Multiply Binomials.** $(x + 3)(x - 2) =$

   Use "FOIL". (First–Out–In–Last): $(x + 3)(x - 2) = x^2 - 2x + 3x - 6$

   Then simplify: $x^2 - 2x + 3x - 6 = x^2 + x - 6$

2) **Multiply Binomials.** $(x - 4)(x - 2) =$

   Use "FOIL". (First–Out–In–Last):

   $(x - 4)(x - 2) = x^2 - 2x - 4x + 8$

   Then simplify: $x^2 - 6x + 8 =$

✎ *Find each product.*

1) $(x - 2)(x + 4) =$

2) $(x + 5)(x - 2) =$

3) $(x - 3)(x - 4) =$

4) $(x + 2)(x + 2) =$

5) $(x - 6)(x - 3) =$

6) $(x + 5)(x + 7) =$

7) $(x + 2)(x - 8) =$

8) $(x - 9)(x + 4) =$

9) $(x + 5)(x + 6) =$

10) $(x - 8)(x + 3) =$

11) $(x + 5)(x + 5) =$

12) $(x + 7)(x + 4) =$

Factoring Trinomials

Step-by-step guide:

- ✓ "FOIL":
$$(x + a)(x + b) = x^2 + (b + a)x + ab$$
- ✓ "Difference of Squares":
$$a^2 - b^2 = (a + b)(a - b)$$
$$a^2 + 2ab + b^2 = (a + b)(a + b)$$
$$a^2 - 2ab + b^2 = (a - b)(a - b)$$
- ✓ "Reverse FOIL":
$$x^2 + (b + a)x + ab = (x + a)(x + b)$$

Example:

1) ***Factor this trinomial.*** $x^2 - 3x - 18 =$
Break the expression into groups: $(x^2 + 3x) + (-6x - 18)$
Now factor out x from $x^2 + 3x : x(x + 2)$, and factor out -6 from $-6x + 18: -6(x + 3)$
Then: $= x(x + 3) - 6(x + 3)$, now factor out like term: $x + 3$
Then: $(x + 3)(x - 6)$

2) ***Factor this trinomial.*** $x^2 + x - 20 =$
Break the expression into groups: $(x^2 - 4x) + (5x - 20)$
Now factor out x from $x^2 - 4x : x(x + 3)$, and factor out 5 from $6x - 18: 5(x - 4)$
Then: $= x(x - 4) + 5(x - 4)$, now factor out like term: $x - 4$
Then: $(x + 5)(x - 4)$

✎ ***Factor each trinomial.***

1) $x^2 + 3x - 10 =$

2) $x^2 - x - 6 =$

3) $x^2 + 8x + 15 =$

4) $x^2 - 7x + 12 =$

5) $x^2 - x - 20 =$

6) $x^2 + 11x + 18 =$

7) $x^2 + 3x - 28 =$

8) $x^2 - 2x - 48 =$

9) $x^2 - 13x + 36 =$

10) $x^2 - x - 56 =$

11) $x^2 - 4x - 45 =$

12) $x^2 - 8x - 48 =$

Operations with Polynomials

Step-by-step guide:

✓ When multiplying a monomial by a polynomial, use the distributive property.

$$a \times (b + c) = a \times b + a \times c$$

Example:

1) **Multiply.** $4(3x - 5) =$

Use the distributive property: $4(3x - 5) = 12x - 20$

2) **Multiply.** $6x(3x + 7) =$

Use the distributive property: $6x(3x + 7) = 18x^2 + 42x$

✎ *Find each product.*

1) $2(3x + 2) =$

2) $-3(2x + 5) =$

3) $4(7x - 3) =$

4) $5(2x - 4) =$

5) $3x(2x - 7) =$

6) $x^2(3x + 4) =$

7) $x^3(x + 5) =$

8) $x^4(5x - 3) =$

9) $4(2x^2 + 3x - 2) =$

10) $-2(x^2 - 6x + 5) =$

11) $5(2x^2 + 4x - 6) =$

12) $-x(3x^2 + 7x + 5) =$

Answers – Chapter 12

Writing Polynomials in Standard Form

1) $-3x$
2) $4x + 5$
3) $-2x^3 + x^2 + 1$
4) $2x^2 + 1$

5) $-2x^3 - x^2 + 4x$
6) $2x^3 - 2x^2 + 12$
7) $9x^4 - 5x + 18$
8) $-2x^3 + 2x^2 + 13x$

9) $-x^3 + 4x^2 + 8$
10) $3x^3 - 2x^2 + 2x$
11) $-6x^3 - 4x^2 + 4x$
12) $-3x^2 - 5x + 2$

Simplifying Polynomials

1) $8x - 12$
2) $15x - 20$
3) $2x^2 - 5x$
4) $20x + 12$

5) $12x^2 - 4x$
6) $3x^2 + 8x$
7) $x^2 + 2x - 8$
8) $x^2 + 5x + 6$

9) $x^2 - 11x + 28$
10) $4x^2 - 2x - 20$
11) $4x^2 - 27x + 18$
12) $6x^2 + 22x + 20$

Adding and Subtracting Polynomials

1) $4x^2 - 6x$
2) $-2x^3 + 2x - 2$
3) $4x^3 - 6$
4) $x^2 - 1$

5) $7x^2$
6) $3x^2 + 8$
7) $10x - 4$
8) $2x^4 - 3x$

9) $-6x^3 - 3x$
10) $3x^3$
11) $-2x^3 + 3x^2 - 5$
12) $x^2 + x$

Multiplying Monomials

1) $10x^7$
2) $-16x^{10}$
3) $10x^3y^4$
4) $-16x^7y^2$

5) $-12x^8y^5$
6) $27x^5y^3$
7) $56x^4y^9$
8) $10x^3y^7$

9) $45x^{11}y^5$
10) $24x^8y^5$
11) $33x^9y^3z^3$
12) $60x^7y^{12}$

Multiplying and Dividing Monomials

1) $x^3 y^3$
2) $2x^9 y^3$
3) $-8x^6 y^4$
4) $-6x^7 y^6$

5) $8x^8 y^7$
6) $18x^9 y^{13}$
7) $-2x^2 y$
8) $4xy^3$

9) $5x^3 y^3$
10) $3x^4 y^8$
11) $5x^4 y^{11}$
12) $-20x^9 y^3$

Multiplying a Polynomial and a Monomial

1) $-10x^2 - 4xy$
2) $6x^2 - 3xy$
3) $4x^2 + 20xy$
4) $-24x^2 + 12x$

5) $-2x^2 + 9xy$
6) $10x^2 - 16xy$
7) $2x^2 + 4xy - 3x$
8) $2x^3 - 4xy^2$

9) $-8x^2 - 16xy$
10) $3x^2 + 21y^2$
11) $-4x^3 y + 8xy$
12) $5x^2 - 20xy + 30$

Multiplying Binomials

1) $x^2 + 2x - 8$
2) $x^2 + 3x - 10$
3) $x^2 - 7x + 12$
4) $x^2 + 4x + 4$

5) $x^2 - 9x + 18$
6) $x^2 + 12x + 35$
7) $x^2 - 6x - 16$
8) $x^2 - 5x - 36$

9) $x^2 + 11x + 30$
10) $x^2 - 5x - 24$
11) $x^2 + 10x + 25$
12) $x^2 + 11x + 28$

Factoring Trinomials

1) $(x - 2)(x + 5)$
2) $(x + 2)(x - 3)$
3) $(x + 5)(x + 3)$
4) $(x - 3)(x - 4)$
5) $(x - 5)(x + 4)$

6) $(x + 2)(x + 9)$
7) $(x + 7)(x - 4)$
8) $(x - 8)(x + 6)$
9) $(x - 4)(x - 9)$
10) $(x - 8)(x +$

7)
11) $(x - 9)(x + 5)$
12) $(x + 4)(x - 12)$

Operations with Polynomials

1) $6x + 4$
2) $-6x - 15$
3) $28x - 12$
4) $10x - 20$

5) $6x^2 - 21x$
6) $3x^3 + 4x^2$
7) $x^4 + 5x^3$
8) $5x^5 - 3x^4$

9) $8x^2 + 12x - 8$
10) $-2x^2 + 12x - 10$
11) $10x^2 + 20x - 30$
12) $-3x^3 - 7x^2 - 5x$

Chapter 13: Geometry and Solid Figures

Math Topics that you'll learn in this Chapter:

- ✓ The Pythagorean Theorem
- ✓ Triangles
- ✓ Polygons
- ✓ Circles
- ✓ Trapezoids
- ✓ Cubes
- ✓ Rectangle Prisms
- ✓ Cylinder

Mathematics is like checkers in being suitable for the young, not too difficult, amusing, and without peril to the state. ~ Plato

The Pythagorean Theorem

Step-by-step guide:

✓ In any right triangle: $a^2 + b^2 = c^2$

Example:

1) Right triangle ABC has two legs of lengths 9 cm (AB) and 12 cm (AC). What is the length of the third side (BC)?

Use Pythagorean Theorem: $a^2 + b^2 = c^2$

Then: $a^2 + b^2 = c^2 \rightarrow 9^2 + 12^2 = c^2 \rightarrow 81 + 144 = c^2$

$c^2 = 225 \rightarrow c = 15 \ cm$

2) Find the missing length.

Use Pythagorean Theorem: $a^2 + b^2 = c^2$

Then: $a^2 + b^2 = c^2 \rightarrow 8^2 + 6^2 = c^2 \rightarrow 64 + 36 = c^2$

$c^2 = 100 \rightarrow c = 10$

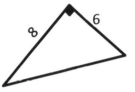

✐ *Find the missing side?*

1)	2)	3)	4)

5 / ? / 12

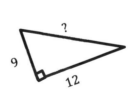

4 / ? / 3

9 / ? / 12

6 / 10 / ?

5)	6)	7)	8)

12 / 15 / ?

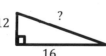

12 / ? / 16

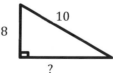

8 / 10 / ?

5 / 13 / ?

Triangles

Step-by-step guide:

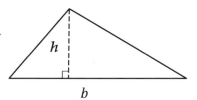

- ✓ In any triangle the sum of all angles is 180 degrees.
- ✓ Area of a triangle = $\frac{1}{2}$ ($base \times height$)

Example:

What is the area of triangles?

1)

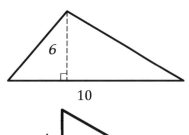

2)

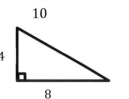

Solution:

Use the are formula: Area = $\frac{1}{2}$ ($base \times height$)

$base = 10$ and $height = 6$

Area = $\frac{1}{2}(10 \times 6) = \frac{1}{2}(60) = 30$

Solution:

Use the are formula: Area = $\frac{1}{2}$ ($base \times height$)

$base = 8$ and $height = 4$

Area = $\frac{1}{2}(8 \times 4) = \frac{32}{2} = 16$

✍ *Find the measure of the unknown angle in each triangle.*

1)

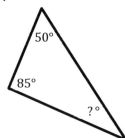

2)

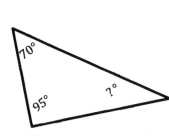

3)

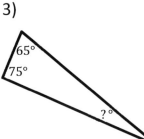

4)

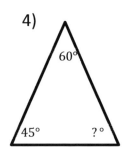

✍ *Find area of each triangle.*

5)

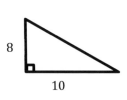

6)

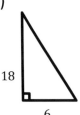

7)

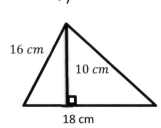

8)

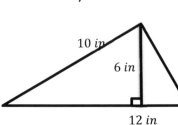

Polygons

Step-by-step guide:

Perimeter of a square $= 4 \times side = 4s$	Perimeter of a rectangle $= 2(width + length)$ width length
Perimeter of trapezoid $= a + b + c + d$ 	Perimeter of a regular hexagon $= 6a$ 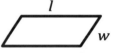
Example: Find the perimeter of following regular hexagon. Perimeter of Pentagon $= 6a$ Perimeter of Pentagon $= 6a = 6 \times 5 = 30\ m$	Perimeter of a parallelogram $= 2(l + w)$

✍ *Find the perimeter of each shape.*

1)   2)   3)   4)

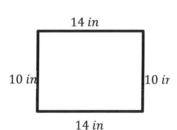   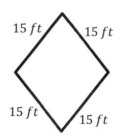   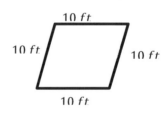

5) Regular   6)   7) Parallelogram   8) Square
hexagon

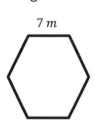   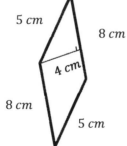   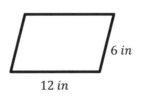   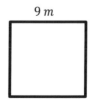

Circles

Step-by-step guide:

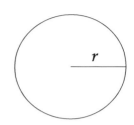

- ✓ In a circle, variable r is usually used for the radius and d for diameter and π is about 3.14.
- ✓ *Area of a circle* $= \pi r^2$
- ✓ *Circumference of a circle* $= 2\pi r$

Example:

1) Find the area of the circle.

Use area formula: $Area = \pi r^2$,

$r = 6\ in$ then: $Area = \pi(6)^2 = 36\pi$, $\quad \pi = 3.14$ **then:** $Area = 36 \times$
$3.14 = 113.04\ in^2$

2) Find the Circumference of the circle.

Use Circumference formula: $Circumference = 2\pi r$

$r = 9\ cm$, then: $Circumference = 2\pi(9) = 18\pi$

$\pi = 3.14$ **then:** $Circumference = 18 \times 3.14 = 56.52\ cm$

✍ ***Complete the table below.*** ($\pi = 3.14$)

	Radius	Diameter	Circumference	Area
Circle 1	4 inches	8 inches	25.12 inches	50.24 square inches
Circle 2		16 meters		
Circle 3				50.24 square ft
Circle 4			50.24 miles	
Circle 5		18 kilometers		
Circle 6	7 centimeters			
Circle 7		9 feet		
Circle 8				19.625 square meters

Trapezoids

Step-by-step guide:

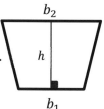

✓ A quadrilateral with at least one pair of parallel sides is a trapezoid.
✓ Area of a trapezoid $= \frac{1}{2}h(b_1 + b_2)$

Example:

Calculate the area of the trapezoid.

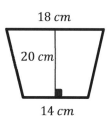

Use area formula: $A = \frac{1}{2}h(b_1 + b_2)$

$b_1 = 14\ cm$, $b_2 = 18\ cm$ and $h = 20\ cm$

Then: $A = \frac{1}{2}(20)(14 + 18) = 10(32) = 320\ cm^2$

✎ *Find the area of each trapezoid.*

1)

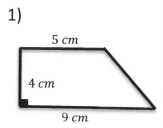

2)

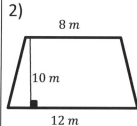

3)

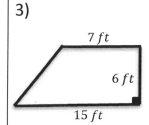

4)

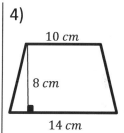

5)

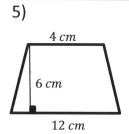

6)

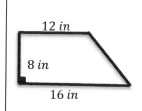

7)

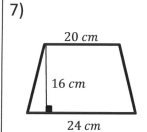

8)

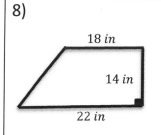

Cubes

Step-by-step guide:

- ✓ A cube is a three-dimensional solid object bounded by six square sides.
- ✓ Volume is the measure of the amount of space inside of a solid figure, like a cube, ball, cylinder or pyramid.
- ✓ Volume of a cube = $(one\ side)^3$
- ✓ surface area of cube = $6 \times (one\ side)^2$

Example:

Find the volume and surface area of this cube.

Use volume formula: $volume = (one\ side)^3$

Then: $volume = (one\ side)^3 = (4)^3 = 64\ cm^3$

Use surface area formula:

$surface\ area\ of\ cube: 6(one\ side)^2 = 6(4)^2 = 6(16) = 96\ cm^2$

4 cm

✍ *Find the volume of each cube.*

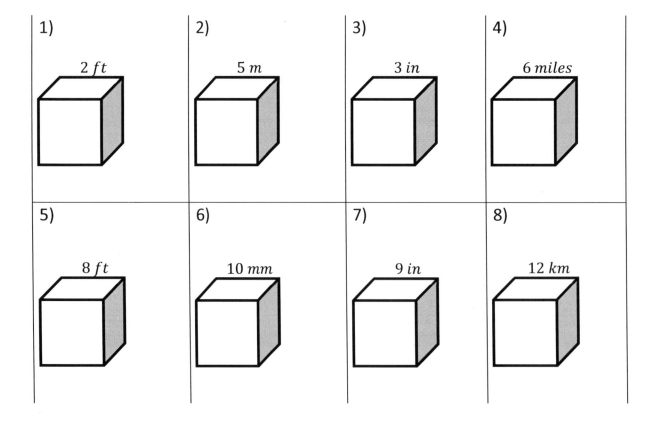

1) 2 ft

2) 5 m

3) 3 in

4) 6 miles

5) 8 ft

6) 10 mm

7) 9 in

8) 12 km

Rectangular Prisms

Step-by-step guide:

✓ A solid 3-dimensional object which has six rectangular faces.
✓ Volume of a Rectangular prism = **Length × Width × Height**

$Volume = l \times w \times h$ $Surface\ area = 2(wh + lw + lh)$

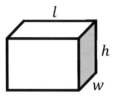

Example:

Find the volume and surface area of rectangular prism.

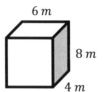

Use volume formula: $Volume = l \times w \times h$

Then: $Volume = 6 \times 4 \times 8 = 192\ m^3$

Use surface area formula: $Surface\ area = 2(wh + lw + lh)$

Then: $Surface\ area = 2\big((4 \times 8) + (6 \times 4) + (6 \times 8)\big)$

$$= 2(32 + 24 + 48) = 2(104) = 208\ m^2$$

✎ Find the volume of each Rectangular Prism.

1)

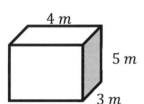

2)

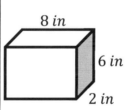

3)

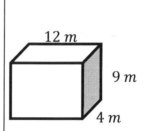

4)

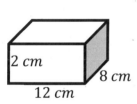

5)

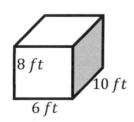

6)

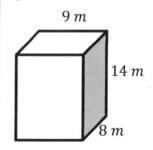

Cylinder

Step-by-step guide:

- ✓ A cylinder is a solid geometric figure with straight parallel sides and a circular or oval cross section.
- ✓ *Volume of Cylinder Formula* $= \pi(radius)^2 \times height$ $\pi =$ 3.14
- ✓ *Surface area of a cylinder* $= 2\pi r^2 + 2\pi rh$

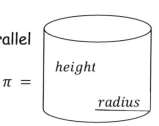

Example:

Find the volume and Surface area of the follow Cylinder.

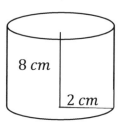

Use volume formula: $Volume = \pi(radius)^2 \times height$
Then: $Volume = \pi(2)^2 \times 8 = \pi 4 \times 8 = 32\pi$
$\pi = 3.14$ **then:** $Volume = 32\pi = 100.48\ cm^3$
Use surface area formula: $Surface\ area = 2\pi r^2 + 2\pi rh$
Then: $= 2\pi(2)^2 + 2\pi(2)(8) = 2\pi(4) + 2\pi(16) = 8\pi + 32\pi = 40\pi$
$\pi = 3.14$ **then:** $Surface\ area = 40 \times 3.14 = 125.6\ cm^2$

✎ *Find the volume of each Cylinder. Round your answer to the nearest tenth.* $(\pi = 3.14)$

1)

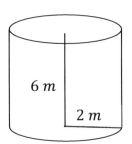

6 m
2 m

2)

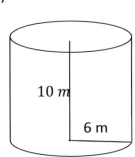

10 m
6 m

3)

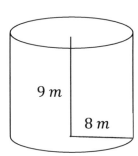

9 m
8 m

4)

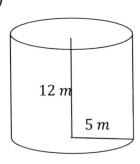

12 m
5 m

5)

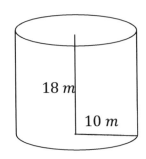

18 m
10 m

6)

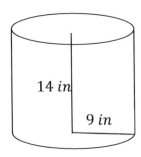

14 in
9 in

Answers – Chapter 13

The Pythagorean Theorem

1) 13
2) 5
3) 15
4) 8

5) 9
6) 20
7) 6
8) 12

Triangles

1) 45°
2) 15°
3) 40°
4) 75°

5) 40 *square unites*
6) 54 *square unites*
7) 90 *square unites*
8) 36 *square unites*

Polygons

1) 32 *cm*
2) 48 *in*
3) 60 *ft*
4) 40 *ft*

5) 42 *m*
6) 26 *cm*
7) 36 *in*
8) 36 *m*

Circles

	Radius	Diameter	Circumference	Area
Circle 1	4 *inches*	8 *inches*	25.12 *inches*	50.24 *square inches*
Circle 2	8 *meters*	16 *meters*	50.24 *meters*	200.96 *square meters*
Circle 3	4 *ft*	8 *ft*	25.12 *ft*	50.24 *square ft*
Circle 4	8 *miles*	16 *miles*	50.24 *miles*	200.96 *square miles*
Circle 5	9 *kilometers*	18 *kilometers*	56.52 *kilometers*	254.34 *sq. kilometers*
Circle 6	7 *centimeters*	14 *centimeters*	43.96 *centimeters*	153.86 *sq. centimeters*
Circle 7	4.5 *feet*	9 *feet*	28.26 *feet*	63.585 *square feet*
Circle 8	2.5 *meters*	5 *meters*	15.7 *meters*	19.625 *square meters*

Trapezoids

1) $28 \ cm^2$
2) $100 \ m^2$
3) $66 \ ft^2$
4) $96 \ cm^2$

5) $48 \ cm^2$
6) $112 \ in^2$
7) $352 \ cm^2$
8) $280 \ in^2$

Cubes

1) $8 \ ft^3$
2) $125 \ m^3$
3) $27 \ in^3$
4) $216 \ miles^3$

5) $512 \ ft^3$
6) $1,000 \ mm^3$
7) $729 \ in^3$
8) $1,728 \ km^3$

Rectangle Prisms

1) $60 \ m^3$
2) $96 \ in^3$
3) $432 \ m^3$

4) $192 \ cm^3$
5) $480 \ ft^3$
6) $1,008 \ m^3$

Cylinder

1) $75.36 \ m^3$
2) $1,130.4 \ m^3$
3) $1,808.64 \ m^3$

4) $942 \ m^3$
5) $5.652 \ m^3$
6) $3,560.76 \ in^3$

Chapter 14:
Statistics

Math Topics that you'll learn in this Chapter:

- ✓ Mean, Median, Mode, and Range of the Given Data

- ✓ Histograms

- ✓ Pie Graph

- ✓ Probability

- ✓ Permutations and Combinations

Millions saw the apple fall, but Newton asked why." - Bernard Baruch

Mean, Median, Mode, and Range of the Given Data

Step-by-step guide:

- ✓ Mean: $\dfrac{\text{sum of the data}}{\text{total number of data entires}}$
- ✓ Mode: value in the list that appears most often
- ✓ Range: the difference of largest value and smallest value in the list

Example:

1) What is the mode of these numbers? $18, 12, 8, 5, 3, 2, 0, 2$

   Mode: value in the list that appears most often
   Therefore: mode is 2

2) What is the median of these numbers? $2, 7, 11, 6, 13, 16, 3$

   Write the numbers in order: $2, 3, 6, 7, 11, 13, 16$

   Median is the number in the middle. Therefore, the median is 7.

✍ *Solve.*

1) Eva went to shop and bought 4 apples, 6 peaches, 3 bananas, 5 pineapple and 8 melons. What are the Mean and Median of her purchase? _____

2) In a javelin throw competition, five athletics score 43, 45, 52, 58 and 62 meters. What are their Mean and Median? _____

✍ *Find Mode and Rage of the Given Data.*

3) $6, 4, 8, 11, 2, 3$

Mode: _____   Range: _____

4) $5, 7, 3, 12, 7, 10, 6, 9, 4$

Mode: _____   Range: _____

5) $10, 10, 6, 7, 10, 7, 13, 15$

Mode: _____   Range: _____

6) $8, 7, 4, 7, 5, 4, 12, 7$

Mode: _____   Range: _____

Histograms

Step-by-step guide:

✓ A histogram is an accurate representation of the distribution of numerical data.

Example:

Use the following Graph to complete the table.

Answer:

Day	Distance (km)
1	
2	

→

Day	Distance (km)
1	378
2	480
3	285
4	536
5	370

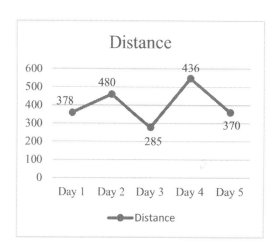

✎ The following table shows the number of births in the US from 2007 to 2012 (in millions).

Year	Number of births (in millions)
2007	4.32
2008	4.25
2009	4.13
2010	4
2011	3.95
2012	3.95

Draw a histogram for the table.

Pie Graph

Step-by-step guide:

✓ A Pie Chart is a circle chart divided into sectors, each sector represents the relative size of each value.

Example:

A library has 670 books that include Mathematics, Physics, Chemistry, English and History. Use following graph to answer question.

What is the number of Mathematics books?

Number of total books $= 670$
Percent of Mathematics books $= 30\% = 0.30$
Then: $0.30 \times 670 = 201$

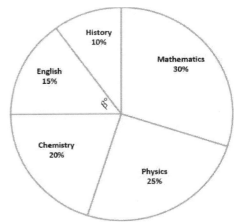

✍ **The circle graph below shows all Jason's expenses for last month. Jason spent $400 on his bills last month.**

1) How much did Jason spend on his car last month? _____

2) How much did Jason spend for foods last month? _____

3) How much did Jason spend on his rent last month? _____

4) What fraction is Jason's expenses for his bills and Car out of his total expenses last month?

Mr. Green's monthly expenses

Probability Problems

Step-by-step guide:

- ✓ Probability is the likelihood of something happening in the future. It is expressed as a number between zero (can never happen) to 1 (will always happen).
- ✓ Probability can be expressed as a fraction, a decimal, or a percent.

Example:

1) If there are 8 red balls and 12 blue balls in a basket, what is the probability that John will pick out a red ball from the basket?

   There are 8 red ball and 20 are total number of balls. Therefore, probability that John will pick out a red ball from the basket is 8 out of 20 or $\frac{8}{8+1} = \frac{8}{20} = \frac{2}{5}$.

2) A bag contains 18 balls: two green, five black, eight blue, a brown, a red and one white. If 17 balls are removed from the bag at random, what is the probability that a brown ball has been removed?

   If 17 balls are removed from the bag at random, there will be one ball in the bag.

   The probability of choosing a brown ball is 1 out of 18. Therefore, the probability of not choosing a brown ball is 17 out of 18 and the probability of having not a brown ball after removing 17 balls is the same.

✎ *Solve.*

1) A number is chosen at random from 1 to 10. Find the probability of selecting number 4 or smaller numbers. _____

2) Bag A contains 9 red marbles and 3 green marbles. Bag B contains 9 black marbles and 6 orange marbles. What is the probability of selecting a green marble at random from bag A? What is the probability of selecting a black marble at random from Bag B? _____ _____

Permutations and Combinations

Step-by-step guide:

✓ Permutations: The number of ways to choose a sample of k elements from a set of n distinct objects where order does matter, and replacements are not allowed. For a permutation problem, use this formula:
$$_nP_k = \frac{n!}{(n-k)!}$$

✓ Combination: The number of ways to choose a sample of r elements from a set of n distinct objects where order does not matter, and replacements are not allowed. For a combination problem, use this formula:
$$_nC_r = \frac{n!}{r!\,(n-r)!}$$

✓ Factorials are products, indicated by an exclamation mark. For example, 4! Equals: $4 \times 3 \times 2 \times 1$. Remember that 0! is defined to be equal to 1.

Examples:

1) How many ways can first and second place be awarded to 10 people?

Since the order matters, we need to use permutation formula where n is 10 and k is 2. Then: $\frac{n!}{(n-k)!} = \frac{10!}{(10-2)!} = \frac{10!}{8!} = \frac{10 \times 9 \times 8!}{8!}$, remove 8! from both sides of the fraction. Then: $\frac{10 \times 9 \times 8!}{8!} = 10 \times 9 = 90$

2) How many ways can we pick a team of 3 people from a group of 8?

Since the order doesn't matter, we need to use combination formula where n is 8 and r is 3. Then: $\frac{n!}{r!\,(n-r)!} = \frac{8!}{3!\,(8-3)!} = \frac{8!}{3!\,(5)!} = \frac{8 \times 7 \times 6 \times 5!}{3!\,(5)!} = \frac{8 \times 7 \times 6}{3 \times 2 \times 1} = \frac{336}{6} = 56$

✐ *Calculate the value of each.*

1) $4! =$ _____
2) $4! \times 3! =$ _____
3) $5! =$ _____
4) $6! + 3! =$ _____

5) $7! =$ _____
6) $8! =$ _____
7) $4! + 4! =$ _____
8) $4! - 3! =$ _____

✐ *Solve each word problems.*

9) Susan is baking cookies. She uses sugar, flour, butter, and eggs. How many different orders of ingredients can she try?

10) Jason is planning for his vacation. He wants to go to museum, watch a movie, go to the beach, and play volleyball. How many different ways of ordering are there for him?

Answers – Chapter 14

Mean, Median, Mode, and Range of the Given Data

1) Mean: 5.2, Median: 5
2) Mean: 52, Median: 52
3) Mode: −, Range: 9
4) Mode: 7, Range: 9
5) Mode: 10, Range: 9
6) Mode: 7, Range: 8

Histograms

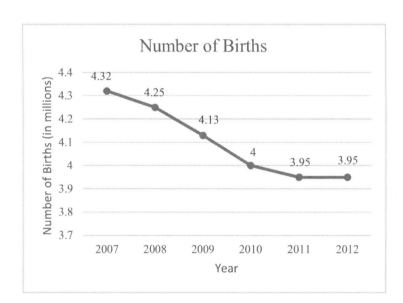

Pie Graph

1) $550
2) $250
3) $675
4) $\frac{19}{50}$

Probability Problems

1) $\frac{2}{5}$
2) $\frac{1}{4}, \frac{3}{5}$

Combinations and Permutations

1) 24
2) 144
3) 120
4) 726
5) 5,040
6) 40,320
7) 48
8) 18
9) 24
10) 24

Chapter 15:
Quadratic

Topics that you'll practice in this chapter:

- ✓ Solve a Quadratic Equation
- ✓ Graphing Quadratic Functions in Vertex Form
- ✓ Solving Quadratic Equations
- ✓ Solve Quadratic Inequalities
- ✓ Graphing Quadratic Inequalities

"Pure mathematics is, in its way, the poetry of logical ideas." -Albert Einstein

Solving a Quadratic Equation

Step-by-step guide:

- ✓ Write the equation in the form of: $ax^2 + bx + c = 0$
- ✓ Factorize the quadratic and solve for the variable.
- ✓ Use quadratic formula if you couldn't factorize the quadratic.
- ✓ Quadratic formula: $x = \frac{-b \pm \sqrt{b^2 - 4ac}}{2a}$

Examples:

Find the solutions of each quadratic.

1) $x^2 + 7x + 10 = 0$

Use quadratic formula: $= \frac{-b \pm \sqrt{b^2 - 4ac}}{2a}$, $a = 1, b = 7$ and $c = 10$

$x = \frac{-7 \pm \sqrt{7^2 - 4.1.10}}{2.1}$, $x_1 = \frac{-7 + \sqrt{7^2 - 4.1.10}}{2.1} = -2$, $x_2 = \frac{-7 - \sqrt{7^2 - 4.1.10}}{2.1} = -5$

2) $x^2 + 4x + 3 = 0$

Use quadratic formula: $= \frac{-b \pm \sqrt{b^2 - 4ac}}{2a}$, $a = 1, b = 4$ and $c = 3$

then: $x = \frac{-4 \pm \sqrt{4^2 - 4.1(3)}}{2(1)}$, $x_1 = \frac{-4 + \sqrt{4^2 - 4.1(3)}}{2(1)} = -1$, $x_2 = \frac{-4 - \sqrt{4^2 - 4.1(3)}}{2(1)} = -3$

✍ *Solve each equation.*

1) $x^2 - 5x - 14 = 0$

2) $x^2 + 8x + 15 = 0$

3) $x^2 - 5x - 36 = 0$

4) $x^2 - 12x - 35 = 0$

5) $x^2 + 12x + 32 = 0$

6) $5x^2 + 27x + 28 = 0$

7) $8x^2 + 26x + 15 = 0$

8) $3x^2 + 10x + 8 = 0$

9) $12x^2 + 30x + 12 = 0$

10) $9x^2 + 57x + 18 = 0$

Graphing Quadratic Functions

Step-by-step guide:

- ✓ Quadratic functions in vertex form: $y = a(x - h)^2 + k$ where (h, k) is the vertex of the function. The axis of symmetry is $x = h$
- ✓ Quadratic functions in standard form: $y = ax^2 + bx + c$ where $x = -\frac{b}{2a}$ is the value of x in the vertex of the function.
- ✓ To graph a quadratic function, first find the vertex, then substitute some values for x and solve for y.

Example:

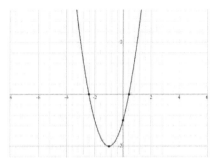

Sketch the graph of $y = (x + 1)^2 - 2$.

The vertex of $y = (x + 1)^2 - 2$ is $(-1, -2)$. Substitute zero for x and solve for y. $y = (0 + 1)^2 - 2 = -1$. The y Intercept is $(0, -1)$.

Now, you can simply graph the quadratic function.

✎ *Sketch the graph of each function. Identify the vertex and axis of symmetry.*

1) $y = 3(x - 5)^2 - 2$

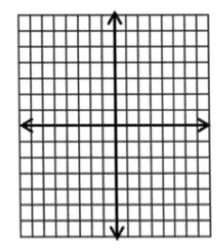

2) $y = x^2 - 3x + 15$

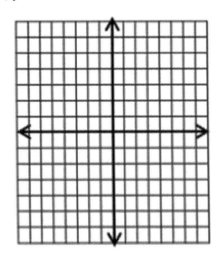

Solving Quadratic Inequalities

Step-by-step guide:

- ✓ A quadratic inequality is one that can be written in one of the following standard forms:

  $$ax^2 + bx + c > 0, \; ax^2 + bx + c < 0, \; ax^2 + bx + c \geq 0, \; ax^2 + bx + c \leq 0$$

- ✓ Solving a quadratic inequality is like solving equations. We need to find the solutions.

Examples:

1) Solve quadratic inequality. $x^2 - 6x + 8 > 0$

   Factor: $x^2 - 6x + 8 > 0 \rightarrow (x - 2)(x - 4) > 0$

   Then the solution could be $x < 2$ or $x > 4$.

2) Solve quadratic inequality. $x^2 - 7x + 10 \geq 0$

   Factor: $x^2 - 7x + 10 \geq 0 \rightarrow (x - 2)(x - 5) \geq 0$. 2 and 5 are the solutions. Now, the solution could be $x < 2$ or $x = 2$ and $x = 5$ or $x > 5$.

✍ *Solve each quadratic inequality.*

1) $x^2 + 7x + 10 < 0$

2) $x^2 + 9x + 20 > 0$

3) $x^2 - 8x + 16 > 0$

4) $x^2 - 8x + 12 \leq 0$

5) $x^2 - 11x + 30 \leq 0$

6) $x^2 - 12x + 27 \geq 0$

7) $x^2 - 16x + 64 \geq 0$

8) $x^2 - 36 \leq 0$

9) $x^2 - 13x + 36 \geq 0$

10) $x^2 + 15x + 36 \leq 0$

11) $4x^2 - 6x - 9 > x^2$

12) $5x^2 - 15x + 10 < 0$

Graphing Quadratic inequalities

Step-by-step guide:

- ✓ A quadratic inequality is in the form $y > ax^2 + bx + c$ (or substitute $<, \leq,$ or $\geq$ for $>$).
- ✓ To graph a quadratic inequality, start by graphing the quadratic parabola. Then fill in the region either inside or outside of it, depending on the inequality.
- ✓ Choose a testing point and check the solution section.

Example: Sketch the graph of $y > 3x^2$.

First, graph $y = 3x^2$

Since, the inequality sing is $>$, we need to use dash lines.

Now, choose a testing point inside the parabola. Let's choose $(0,2)$. $y > 3x^2 \rightarrow 2 > 3(0)^2 \rightarrow 3 > 0$

This is true. So, inside the parabola is the solution section.

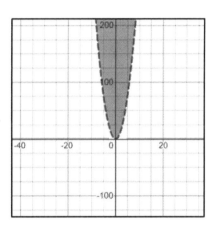

✍️Sketch the graph of each function.

1) $y < -2x^2$

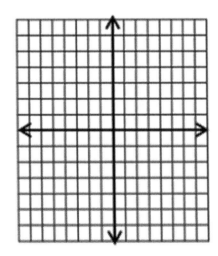

2) $y \geq 4x^2$

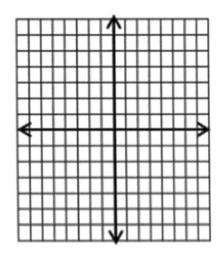

Answers of Worksheets – Chapter 15

Solving a Quadratic Equation

1) $x = -2, x = 7$
2) $x = -3, x = -5$
3) $x = 9, x = -4$
4) $x = 7, x = 5$
5) $x = -4, x = -8$
6) $x = -\frac{7}{5}, x = -4$

7) $x = -\frac{5}{2}, x = -\frac{3}{4}$
8) $x = -\frac{4}{3}, x = -2$
9) $x = -\frac{1}{2}, x = -2$
10) $x = -\frac{1}{3}, x = -6$

Graphing quadratic functions in vertex form

1)

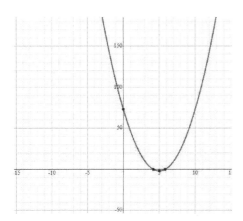

2)

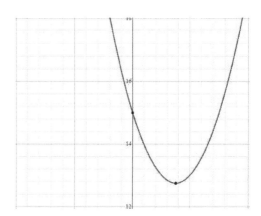

Solve quadratic inequalities

1) $-5 < x < -2$
2) $x < -5 \ or \ x > -4$
3) $x < 4 \ or \ x > 4$
4) $2 \leq x \leq 6$
5) $5 \leq x \leq 6$
6) $x \leq 3 or \ x \geq 9$

7) *all real numbers*
8) $-6 \leq x \leq 6$
9) $x \leq 4 \ or \ x \geq 9$
10) $-12 \leq x \leq -3$
11) $x < -1 \ or \ x > 3$
12) $1 < x < 2$

Graphing quadratic inequalities

1)

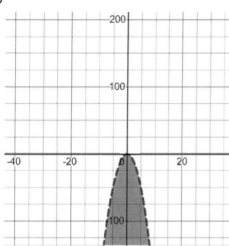

2)

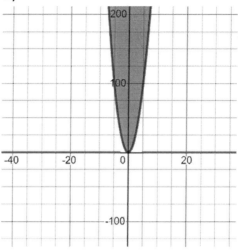

Chapter 16:
Complex Numbers

Math Topics that you'll learn in this Chapter:

✓ Adding and Subtracting Complex Numbers

✓ Multiplying and Dividing Complex Numbers

✓ Rationalizing Imaginary Denominators

Mathematics is a hard thing to love. It has the unfortunate habit, like a rude dog, of turning its most unfavorable side towards you when you first make contact with it. – David Whiteland

Adding and Subtracting Complex Numbers

Step-by-step guide:

- ✓ A complex number is expressed in the form $a + bi$, where a and b are real numbers, and i, which is called an imaginary number, is a solution of the equation $x^2 = -1$
- ✓ For adding complex numbers: $(a + bi) + (c + di) = (a + c) + (b + d)i$
- ✓ For subtracting complex numbers: $(a + bi) - (c + di) = (a - c) + (b - d)i$

Examples:

1) Solve: $10 + (-5 - 3i) - 2$

   Remove parentheses: $10 + (-5 - 3i) - 2 \rightarrow 10 - 5 - 3i - 2$

   Combine like terms: $10 - 5 - 3i - 2 = 3 - 3i$

2) Solve: $-3 + (4i) + (9 - 2i)$

   Remove parentheses: $-3 + (4i) + (9 - 2i) \rightarrow -3 + 4i + 9 - 2i$

   Group like terms: $-3 + 4i + 9 - 2i \rightarrow 6 + 2i$

✍ *Simplify.*

1) $(1 - 2i) + (-4i) =$

2) $12 + (2 - 6i) =$

3) $-5 + (-2 - 8i) =$

4) $(-4i) - (7 - 2i) =$

5) $(-3 - 2i) - (2i) =$

6) $(8 - 6i) + (-5i) =$

7) $(-3 + 6i) - (-9 - i) =$

8) $(-5 + 15i) - (-3 + 3i) =$

9) $(-14 + i) - (-12 - 11i) =$

10) $(-18 - 3i) + (11 + 5i) =$

11) $(-11 - 9i) - (-9 - 3i) =$

12) $-8 + (2i) + (-8 + 6i) =$

Multiplying and Dividing Complex Numbers

Step-by-step guide:

- ✓ Multiplying complex numbers: $(a + bi) + (c + di) = (ac - bd) + (ad + bc)i$

- ✓ Dividing complex numbers: $\frac{a+bi}{c+di} = \frac{a+bi}{c+di} \times \frac{c-di}{c-di} = \frac{ac+b}{c^2-d^2} + \frac{bc+a}{c^2-d^2}i$

- ✓ Imaginary number rule: $i^2 = -1$

Examples:

1) Solve: $\frac{4-2i}{2+i} =$

Use the rule for dividing complex numbers:

$$\frac{a+bi}{c+di} = \frac{a+bi}{c+di} \times \frac{c-di}{c-di} = \frac{ac+bd}{c^2-d^2} + \frac{bc+ad}{c^2-d^2}i \rightarrow$$

$$\frac{4-2i}{2+i} \times \frac{2-i}{2-i} = \frac{(4\times(2)+(-2)(1)}{2^2+(1)^2} + \frac{(-2\times(2)-(4)(1)}{2^2+(1)^2}i = \frac{6-8i}{5} = \frac{6}{5} - \frac{8}{5}i$$

2) Solve: $(2 - 3i)(4 - 3i)$

Use the rule: $(a + bi) + (c + di) = (ac - bd) + (ad + bc)i$

$$\left(2.4 - (-3)(-3)\right) + (2(-3) + (-3).4)i = -1 - 18i$$

✎ *Simplify.*

1) $(-2 - i)(4 + i) =$

2) $(2 - 2i)^2 =$

3) $(4 - 3i)(6 - 6i) =$

4) $(5 + 4i)^2 =$

5) $(4i)(-i)(2 - 5i) =$

6) $(2 - 8i)(3 - 5i) =$

7) $\frac{9i}{3-i} =$

8) $\frac{2+4i}{14+4i} =$

9) $\frac{5+6i}{-1+8i} =$

10) $\frac{-8-i}{-4-6i} =$

11) $\frac{-1+5i}{-8-7i} =$

12) $\frac{-2-9i}{-2+7i} =$

Rationalizing Imaginary Denominators

Step-by-step guide:

- ✓ Step 1: Find the conjugate (it's the denominator with different sign between the two terms.
- ✓ Step 2: Multiply numerator and denominator by the conjugate.
- ✓ Step 3: Simplify if needed.

Examples:

1) Solve: $\frac{2-3i}{6i}$

Multiply by the conjugate: $\frac{-i}{-i} \cdot \frac{2-3i}{6i} = \frac{(2-3i)(-i)}{6i(-i)} = \frac{-3-2i}{6} = -\frac{1}{2} - \frac{1}{3}i$

2) Solve: $\frac{8i}{2-4i}$

Factor $2 - 4i = 2(1-2i)$, then: $\frac{8i}{2(1-2i)} = \frac{4i}{(1-2i)}$

Multiply by the conjugate $\frac{1+2i}{1+2i}$: $\frac{4i(1+2i)}{(1-2i)(1+2i)} = \frac{-8+4i}{5} = -\frac{8}{5} + \frac{4}{5}i$

✎ **Simplify.**

1) $\frac{-8}{-5i} =$

2) $\frac{-5}{-i} =$

3) $\frac{3}{5i} =$

4) $\frac{6}{-4i} =$

5) $\frac{-6-i}{-1+6i} =$

6) $\frac{-9-3i}{-3+3i} =$

7) $\frac{4i+1}{-1+3i} =$

8) $\frac{6-3i}{2-i} =$

9) $\frac{-5+2i}{2-3i} =$

10) $\frac{-9-i}{2-i} =$

11) $\frac{-10-5}{-6+6i} =$

12) $\frac{-5-9i}{9+8i} =$

Answers of Worksheets – Chapter 16

Adding and subtracting complex numbers

1) $1 - 6i$
2) $14 - 6i$
3) $-7 - 8i$
4) $-7 - 2i$

5) $-3 - 4i$
6) $8 - 11i$
7) $6 + 7i$
8) $-2 + 12i$

9) $-2 + 12i$
10) $-7 + 2i$
11) $-2 - 6i$
12) $-16 + 8i$

Multiplying and dividing complex numbers

1) $-7 - 6i$
2) $-8i$
3) $6 - 42i$
4) $9 + 40i$
5) $8 - 20i$
6) $-34 - 34i$

7) $-\dfrac{9}{10} + \dfrac{27}{10}i$
8) $\dfrac{11}{53} + \dfrac{12}{53}i$
9) $\dfrac{43}{65} - \dfrac{46}{65}i$

10) $\dfrac{19}{26} + \dfrac{11}{13}i$
11) $-\dfrac{27}{113} - \dfrac{47}{113}i$
12) $-\dfrac{59}{53} + \dfrac{32}{53}i$

Rationalizing imaginary denominators

1) $\dfrac{-8}{5}i$
2) $-5i$
3) $-\dfrac{3}{5}i$
4) $\dfrac{3}{2}i$
5) i

6) $1 + 2i$
7) $\dfrac{11}{10} - \dfrac{7}{10}i$
8) 3
9) $-\dfrac{16}{13} - \dfrac{11}{13}i$
10) $-\dfrac{17}{5} + \dfrac{11}{5}i$

11) $\dfrac{5}{12} + \dfrac{5}{4}i$
12) $-\dfrac{117}{145} - \dfrac{41}{145}i$

Chapter 17:
Functions

Math Topics that you'll learn in this Chapter:

- ✓ Function Notation

- ✓ Adding and Subtracting Functions

- ✓ Multiplying and Dividing Functions

- ✓ Composition of Functions

"The mathematician does not study pure mathematics because it is useful; he studies it because he delights in it and he

delights in it because it is beautiful" Georg Cantor

Function Notation

Step-by-step guide:

- ✓ Functions are mathematical operations that assign unique outputs to given inputs.
- ✓ Function notation is the way a function is written. It is meant to be a precise way of giving information about the function without a rather lengthy written explanation.
- ✓ The most popular function notation is $f(x)$ which is read "f of x".

Examples:

1) Evaluate: $h(n) = n^2 - 2$, find $h(4)$. Substitute x with 4:

Then: $h(n) = n^2 - 2 \rightarrow h(4) = (4)^2 - 2 \rightarrow h(4) = 16 - 2 \rightarrow h(4) = 14$

2) Evaluate: $w(x) = 4x - 1$, find $w(2)$. Substitute x with 4: Then: $w(x) = 4x - 1 \rightarrow w(2) = 4(2) - 1 \rightarrow w(2) = 8 - 1 \rightarrow w(2) = 7$

🖎 *Evaluate each function.*

1) $f(x) = 2x + 8$, find $f(-1)$

2) $g(n) = n + 12$, find $g(2)$

3) $g(n) = -2n + 3$, find $g(-2)$

4) $h(n) = -2n^2 - 6n$, find $h(-1)$

5) $g(a) = 3a^2 + 2a$, find $g(3)$

6) $h(x) = x^2 + 1$, find $h(-2)$

7) $h(x) = x^3 + 8$, find $h(-1)$

8) $h(x) = 2x^2 - 10$, find $h(4)$

9) $h(a) = -2a - 5$, find $h(3)$

10) $k(a) = -7a + 3$, find $k(-2)$

11) $h(x) = 4x + 5$, find $h(6)$

12) $h(n) = -n^2 - 10$, find $h(5)$

Adding and Subtracting Functions

Step-by-step guide:

✓ Just like we can add and subtract numbers, we can add and subtract functions. For example, if we had functions f and g, we could create two new functions:
✓ f + g and f - g.

Examples:

1) $g(a) = a - 1, f(a) = a + 5,$ **Find:** $(g + f)(-1)$

$(g + f)(a) = g(a) + f(a),$ **Then:** $(g + f)(a) = a - 1 + a + 5 = 2a + 4$

Substitute a with -1: $(g + f)(a) = 2a + 4 = 2(-1) + 4 = -2 + 4 = 2$

2) $f(x) = 3x - 3, g(x) = x - 5,$ **Find:** $(f - g)(3)$

$(f - g)(x) = f(x) - g(x),$ **then:** $(f - g)(x) = 3x - 3 - (x - 5) = 3x - 3 - x + 5$

$$= 2x + 2$$

Substitute x with 3: $(f - g)(1) = 2(3) + 2 = 8$

✎ *Perform the indicated operation.*

1) $g(x) = x + 2$

  $h(x) = 2x + 3$

  Find: $g(-1) - h(-1)$

2) $h(x) = 2x + 1$

  $g(x) = -x + 4$

  Find: $(h + g)(2)$

3) $f(x) = 2x^2 - 1$

  $g(x) = x^2 + 2$

  Find: $(f - g)(-1)$

4) $h(n) = -n^2 + 3$

  $g(n) = -n + 9$

  Find: $(h - g)(3)$

5) $g(x) = x^2 - 1$

  $f(x) = 2x + 12$

  Find: $(g - f)(2)$

6) $g(x) = 2x^3 + 8$

  $f(x) = -2x^2 - 10$

  Find: $(g + f)(2)$

Multiplying and Dividing Functions

Step-by-step guide:

✓ Just like we can multiply and divide numbers, we can multiply and divide functions. For example, if we had functions f and g, we could create two new functions: f × g, and $\frac{f}{g}$.

Examples:

1) $g(x) = x + 1, f(x) = x - 2$, Find: $(g.f)(2)$

$(g.f)(x) = g(x).f(x) = (x + 1)(x - 2) = x^2 - 2x + x - 2 = x^2 - x - 2$

Substitute x with 2:

$(g.f)(x) = x^2 - x - 2 = (2)^2 - 2 - 2 = 4 - 2 - 2 = 0$

2) $f(x) = x - 2, h(x) = x + 8$, Find: $\left(\frac{f}{h}\right)(-1)$

$\left(\frac{f}{h}\right)(x) = \frac{f(x)}{h(x)} = \frac{x-2}{x+8}$

Substitute x with -1: $\left(\frac{f}{h}\right)(x) = \frac{x-2}{x+8} = \frac{(-1)-2}{(-1)+8} = \frac{-3}{7} = -\frac{3}{7}$

✎ *Perform the indicated operation.*

1) $f(x) = x - 1$

$g(x) = x + 4$

Find $(\frac{f}{g})(2)$

2) $g(a) = 2a + 6$

$f(a) = a - 12$

Find $(\frac{g}{f})(4)$

3) $g(x) = 2x + 4$

$h(x) = x - 3$

Find $(g.h)(-1)$

4) $g(n) = n^2 + 6$

$h(n) = 2n - 8$

Find $(g.h)(2)$

5) $f(x) = x^2 - 2$

$g(x) = x + 1$

Find $(f.g)(2)$

6) $f(x) = 2a^2 + 4$

$g(x) = 6 + 2a$

Find $(\frac{f}{g})(2)$

Composition of Functions

Step-by-step guide:

- ✓ The term "composition of functions" (or "composite function") refers to the combining together of two or more functions in a manner where the output from one function becomes the input for the next function.
- ✓ The notation used for composition is: $(f \circ g)(x) = f(g(x))$

Examples:

1) *Using* f(x) = x − 2 *and* g(x) = x, *find:* $f(g(2))$

$(f \circ g)(x) = f(g(x))$

Then: $(f \circ g)(x) = f(g(x)) = f(x) = x - 2$

Substitute x with 2: $(f \circ g)(2) = 2 - 2 = 0$

2) *Using* f(x) = x + 8 *and* g(x) = x − 2, *find:* $g(f(4))$

$(f \circ g)(x) = f(g(x))$

Then: $(g \circ f)(x) = g(f(x)) = g(x + 8)$, *now substitute* x *in* f(x) *by* x + 8. *Then:* $g(x + 8) = (x + 8) - 2 = x + 8 - 2 = x + 6$

Substitute x with 4: $(g \circ f)(4) = g(f(x)) = 4 + 6 = 10$

✎ *Using* f(x) = x + 2 *and* g(x) = x − 1, *find:*

1) $f(g(1))$

3) $g(f(-1))$

2) $f(f(-2))$

4) $g(g(2))$

✎ *Using* f(x) = 5x + 2 *and* g(x) = x − 6, *find:*

5) $f(g(-1))$

7) $g(f(-2))$

6) $f(f(2))$

8) $g(g(5))$

Answers of Worksheets – Chapter 17

Function Notation

1) 6

2) 14

3) 7

4) 4

5) 33

6) 5

7) 7

8) 22

9) −11

10) −11

11) 29

12) −35

Adding and Subtracting Functions

1) 0

2) 7

3) −13

4) −2

5) −12

6) 6

Multiplying and Dividing Functions

1) $\frac{1}{6}$

2) −8

3) 6

4) $-\frac{7}{4}$

5) −40

6) $\frac{6}{5}$

Composition of functions

1) 2

2) 2

3) 0

4) 0

5) −33

6) 62

7) −14

8) −7

Chapter 18:
Trigonometric Functions

Math Topics that you'll learn in this Chapter:

- ✓ Trig Ratios of General Angles
- ✓ Conterminal Angles and Reference Angles
- ✓ Angles and Angle Measure
- ✓ Evaluating Trigonometric Function
- ✓ Missing Sides and Angles of a Right Triangle
- ✓ Arc length and Sector Area

Trig Ratios of General Angles

Step-by-step guide:

✓ Learn common trigonometric functions:

θ	0°	30°	45°	60°	90°
$\sin\theta$	0	$\dfrac{1}{2}$	$\dfrac{\sqrt{2}}{2}$	$\dfrac{\sqrt{3}}{2}$	1
$\cos\theta$	1	$\dfrac{\sqrt{3}}{2}$	$\dfrac{\sqrt{2}}{2}$	$\dfrac{1}{2}$	0
$\tan\theta$	0	$\dfrac{\sqrt{3}}{3}$	1	$\sqrt{3}$	Undefined

Examples:

Find each trigonometric function.

1) $\cos 120°$

   Use the following property: $cos(x) = sin(90° - x)$

   $\cos 120° = sin(90° - 120°) = \sin(-30°) = -\dfrac{1}{2}$

2) $\sin 135°$.

   Use the following property: $sin(x) = cos(90° - x)$

   $\sin 135° = cos(90° - 135°) = cos(-45°)$

   Now use the following property: $cos(-x) = \cos(x)$

   $cos(-45°) = cos(45°) = \dfrac{\sqrt{2}}{2}$

✍ Evaluate.

1) $\sin 120° = $ _____

2) $\sin -330° = $ _____

3) $\tan -90° = $ _____

4) $\cot 90° = $ _____

5) $\cos -90° = $ _____

6) $\sec 60° = $ _____

7) $\csc 480° = $ _____

8) $\cot -135° = $ _____

Conterminal Angles and Reference Angles

Step-by-step guide:

- ✓ Conterminal angles are equal angles.
- ✓ To find a conterminal of an angle, add or subtract 360 degrees (or 2π for radians) to the given angle.
- ✓ Reference angle is the smallest angle that you can make from the terminal side of an angle with the x-axis.

Examples:

1) Find a positive and a negative conterminal angles to angle $65°$.

$65° - 360° = -295°$

$65° + 360° = 435°$

$-295°$ and a $435°$ are conterminal with a $65°$.

2) Find a positive and negative conterminal angles to angle $\frac{\pi}{2}$.

$\frac{\pi}{2} + 2\pi = \frac{5\pi}{2}$

$\frac{\pi}{2} - 2\pi = -\frac{3\pi}{2}$

✎ *Find a conterminal angle between* $0°$ *and* $360°$ *for each angle provided.*

1) $-310° =$ 3) $-440° =$

2) $-325° =$ 4) $640° =$

✎ *Find a conterminal angle between* 0 *and* 2π *for each given angle.*

5) $\frac{14\pi}{5} =$ 7) $\frac{13}{18} =$

6) $-\frac{16\pi}{9} =$ 8) $\frac{19\pi}{12} =$

Angles and Angle Measure

Step-by-step guide:

- ✓ To convert degrees to radians, use this formula: $\boldsymbol{Radians = Degrees \times \frac{\pi}{180}}$
- ✓ To convert radians to degrees, use this formula: $\boldsymbol{Degrees = Radians \times \frac{180}{\pi}}$

Examples:

1) Convert 120 degrees to radians.

Use this formula: $Radians = Degrees \times \frac{\pi}{180}$

$$Radians = 120 \times \frac{\pi}{180} = \frac{120\pi}{180} = \frac{2\pi}{3}$$

2) Convert $\frac{\pi}{3}$ to degrees.

Use this formula: $Degrees = Radians \times \frac{\pi}{180}$

$$Radians = \frac{\pi}{3} \times \frac{180}{\pi} = \frac{180\pi}{3\pi} = 60$$

✍ *Convert each degree measure into radians.*

1) $-150° = $ ____

2) $420° = $ ____

3) $300° = $ ____

4) $-60° = $ ____

5) $315° = $ ____

6) $600° = $ ____

✍ *Convert each radian measure into degrees.*

7) $-\frac{16\pi}{3} = $

8) $-\frac{3\pi}{5} = $

9) $\frac{11\pi}{6} = $

10) $\frac{5\pi}{9} = $

11) $-\frac{\pi}{3} = $

12) $\frac{13\pi}{6} = $

Evaluating Trigonometric Function

Step-by-step guide:

- ✓ Step 1: Draw the terminal side of the angle.
- ✓ Step 2: Find reference angle. (It is the smallest angle that you can make from the terminal side of an angle with the x-axis.)
- ✓ Step 3: Find the trigonometric function of the reference angle.

Examples:

1) *Find the exact value of trigonometric function.* $\tan \frac{7\pi}{6}$

   Rewrite the angles for $an \frac{4\pi}{3}$:

   $$\tan \frac{4\pi}{3} = \tan \left(\frac{3\pi+\pi}{3}\right) = \tan \left(\pi + \frac{1}{3}\pi\right)$$

   Use the periodicity of tan: $\tan(x + \pi . k) = \tan(x)$

   $$\tan \left(\pi + \frac{1}{3}\pi\right) = \tan \left(\frac{1}{3}\pi\right) = \sqrt{3}$$

2) *Find the exact value of trigonometric function.* $\cos 270°$

   Write $\cos (270°)$ as $\cos (180° + 90°)$. Recall that $\cos 180° = -1, \cos 90° = 0$

   The reference angle of 270° is 90°. Therefore, $\cos 90° = 0$

✎ *Find the exact value of each trigonometric function.*

1) $\cot - 495° = $ _____

2) $\tan 405° = $ _____

3) $\cot 390° = $ _____

4) $\cos - 300° = $ _____

5) $\cot - 210° = $ _____

6) $\tan \frac{7\pi}{6} = $ _____

7) $\tan - \frac{\pi}{6} = $ _____

8) $\cot - \frac{7\pi}{6} = $ _____

146

Missing Sides and Angles of a Right Triangle

Step-by-step guide:
- ✓ By using Sine, Cosine or Tangent, we can find an unknown side in a right triangle when we have one length, and one angle (apart from the right angle).
- ✓ Adjacent, Opposite and Hypotenuse, in a right triangle is shown below.
- ✓ Recall the three main trigonometric functions:

SOH − CAH − TOA, $sin\ \theta = \frac{opposite}{hypotenuse}$, $Cos\ \theta = \frac{adjacent}{hypotenuse}$, $\tan\theta = \frac{opposite}{adjacent}$

Example:

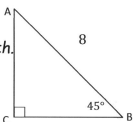

Find AC in the following triangle. Round answers to the nearest tenth.

$sin\ \theta = \frac{opposite}{hypotenuse}$. $sine\ 45° = \frac{AC}{8} \rightarrow 8 \times sin\ 45° = AC$,

now use a calculator to find $sin\ 45°$. $sin\ 40° = \frac{\sqrt{2}}{2} \rightarrow AC \cong 0.70710$

✎ *Find the measure of each angle indicated.*

1)

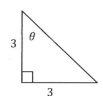

2)

✎ *Find the missing sides. Round answers to the nearest tenth.*

3)

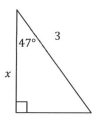

4)

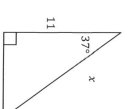

5)

6)

Arc length and Sector Area

Step-by-step guide:

✓ To find a sector of a circle, use this formula: $Area\ of\ a\ sector = \pi r^2(\frac{\theta}{360})$, r is the radius of the circle and θ is the central angle of the sector.

✓ To find the arc of a sector of a circle, use this formula: $Arc\ of\ a\ sector = (\frac{\theta}{180})\pi r$

Examples:

1) *Find the length of the arc. Round your answers to the nearest tenth.* ($\pi = 3.14$) $r = 24$ cm, $\theta = 60°$

Use this formula: $length\ of\ a\ sector = (\frac{\theta}{180})\pi r$

$length\ of\ a\ sector = \left(\frac{60}{180}\right)\pi(24) = \left(\frac{1}{3}\right)\pi(24) = 8 \times 3.14 \cong 25.12\ cm$

2) *Find the area of the sector.* $r = 6$ ft, $\theta = 90°$

Use this formula: $Area\ of\ a\ sector = \pi r^2(\frac{\theta}{360})$

$Area\ of\ a\ sector = \pi r^2\left(\frac{\theta}{360}\right) = (3.14)(6^2)\left(\frac{90}{360}\right) = (3.14)(36)\left(\frac{1}{4}\right) \cong 28.26$

✎ *Find the length of each arc. Round your answers to the nearest tenth.*

1) $r = 14$ ft, $\theta = 45°$

2) $r = 18\ m$, $\theta = 60°$

3) $r = 26\ m$, $\theta = 90°$

4) $r = 20\ m$, $\theta = 120°$

✎ *Find the area of the sector.*

5) $r = 4\ m$, $\theta = 20°$

6) $r = 2\ m$, $\theta = 45°$

7) $r = 8\ m$, $\theta = 90°$

8) $r = 4\ m$, $\theta = 135°$

Answers of Worksheets – Chapter 18

Trig ratios of general angles

1) $\frac{\sqrt{3}}{2}$

2) $\frac{1}{2}$

3) Undefined

4) 0

5) 0

6) 2

7) $\frac{2\sqrt{3}}{3}$

8) 1

Co–Terminal Angles and Reference Angles

1) 50°

2) 35°

3) 280°

4) 280°

5) $\frac{4\pi}{5}$

6) $\frac{2\pi}{9}$

7) $\frac{5\pi}{18}$

8) $\frac{5\pi}{12}$

Angles and Angle Measure

1) $-\frac{5\pi}{6}$

2) $\frac{7\pi}{3}$

3) $\frac{5\pi}{3}$

4) $-\frac{\pi}{3}$

5) $\frac{7\pi}{4}$

6) $\frac{10\pi}{3}$

7) $-960°$

8) $-108°$

9) 330°

10) 100°

11) $-60°$

12) 390°

Evaluating Trigonometric Expression

1) 1

2) 1

3) $\sqrt{3}$

4) $\frac{1}{2}$

5) $-\sqrt{3}$

6) $\frac{\sqrt{3}}{3}$

7) $-\frac{\sqrt{3}}{3}$

8) $-\sqrt{3}$

Missing sides and angles of a right triangle

1) 45°

2) 48.2°

3) 2

4) 13.8

5) 6.7

6) 12.8

Arc length and sector area

1) 10.99

2) 18.84

3) 40.82

4) 41.5

5) 2.8

6) 1.57

7) 50.24

8) 18.84

Time to Test

Time to refine your skill with a practice examination

Take a REAL ALEKS Mathematics test to simulate the test day experience. After you've finished, score your test using the answers and explanations section.

Before You Start

- You'll need a pencil and scratch papers to take the test.

- For these practice tests, don't time yourself. Spend time as much as you need.

- After you've finished the test, review the answer key to see where you went wrong.

Good Luck!

ALEKS Mathematics Practice Test 1

2020

Total number of questions: 30

Total time (Calculator): No time limit

Calculators are permitted for ALEKS Math Test.

1) If $f(x) = 4x - 2$ and $g(x) = x^2 - x$, then find $(\frac{f}{g})(x)$.

2) A bank is offering 4.5% simple interest on a savings account. If you deposit $12,000, how much interest will you earn in two years?

3) If the ratio of home fans to visiting fans in a crowd is $3:2$ and all $24,000$ seats in a stadium are filled, how many visiting fans are in attendance?

4) If the interior angles of a quadrilateral are in the ratio $2:3:3:4$, what is the measure of the largest angle?

5) If the area of a circle is 49 square meters, what is its diameter?

6) The length of a rectangle is $\frac{5}{4}$ times its width. If the width is 20, what is the perimeter of this rectangle?

7) In the figure below, line A is parallel to line B. What is the value of angle x?

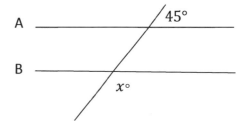

8) An angle is equal to one ninth of its supplement. What is the measure of that angle?

9) What is the value of y in the following system of equations?
$$2x + 5y = 11$$
$$4x - 2y = -14$$

10) Last week 25,000 fans attended a football match. This week three times as many bought tickets, but one sixth of them cancelled their tickets. How many are attending this week?

11) If $sin\ A = \frac{1}{3}$ in a right triangle and the angle A is an acute angle, then what is $cos\ A$?

12) In the standard (x, y) coordinate system plane, what is the area of the circle with the following equation?
$$(x + 2)^2 + (y - 4)^2 = 25$$

13) Convert 580,000 to scientific notation.

14) The ratio of boys to girls in a school is 2: 3. If there are 500 students in a school, how many boys are in the school.

15) If 150% of a number is 75, then what is 80% of that number?

16) If $A = \begin{bmatrix} -1 & 2 \\ 1 & -2 \end{bmatrix}$ and $B = \begin{bmatrix} 3 & 1 \\ -2 & 3 \end{bmatrix}$, then $2A - B =$

17) What is the solution of the following inequality?

$$|x - 2| \geq 4$$

18) If $\tan x = \frac{8}{15}$, then $\sin x =$

19) $(x^6)^{\frac{7}{8}}$ equal to?

20) What are the zeroes of the function $f(x) = x^3 + 5x^2 + 6x$?

21) If $x + sin^2a + cos^2a = 3$, then $x = ?$

22) If $\sqrt{5x} = \sqrt{y}$, then $x =$

23) The average weight of 18 girls in a class is $55\ kg$ and the average weight of 32 boys in the same class is $62\ kg$. What is the average weight of all the 50 students in that class?

24) What is the value of the expression $5(x - 2y) + (2 - x)^2$ when $x = 3$ and $y = -3$?

25) Sophia purchased a sofa for $530.40. The sofa is regularly priced at $631. What was the percent discount Sophia received on the sofa?

26) If one angle of a right triangle measures 60°, what is the sine of the other acute angle?

27) Simplify $\frac{4-3i}{-4i}$?

28) The average of five consecutive numbers is 40. What is the smallest number?

29) What is the slope of a line that is perpendicular to the line
$$4x - 2y = 14?$$

30) If $f(x)=2x^3+ 4$ and $(x) = \frac{1}{x}$, what is the value of $f(g(x))$?

This is the end of Practice Test 1.

ALEKS Mathematics
Practice Test 2

2020

Total number of questions: 30

Total time (Calculator): No time limit

Calculators are permitted for ALEKS Math Test.

(On a real ALEKS test, there is an onscreen calculator to use.)

1) How many tiles of $8\ cm^2$ is needed to cover a floor of dimension $6\ cm$ by $24\ cm$?

2) What is the area of a square whose diagonal is $8\ cm$?

3) What is the value of x in the following figure?

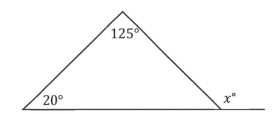

4) What is the value of y in the following system of equation?
$$3x - 4y = -20$$
$$-x + 2y = 10$$

5) How long does a 420–miles trip take moving at 50 miles per hour (mph)?

6) When 40% of 60 is added to 12% of 600, the resulting number is:

7) What is the solution of the following inequality?
$$|x - 10| \leq 3$$

8) In the following figure, ABCD is a rectangle, and E and F are points on AD and DC, respectively. The area of ΔBED is 16, and the area of ΔBDF is 18. What is the perimeter of the rectangle?

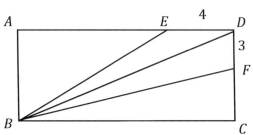

9) If a tree casts a 24–foot shadow at the same time that a 3 feet yardstick casts a 2–foot shadow, what is the height of the tree?

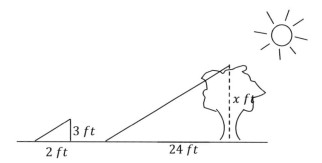

10) A ladder leans against a wall forming a $60°$ angle between the ground and the ladder. If the bottom of the ladder is 30 feet away from the wall, how long is the ladder?

11) Simplify.

$$2x^2 + 3y^5 - x^2 + 2z^3 - 2y^2 + 2x^3 - 2y^5 + 5z^3$$

12) In five successive hours, a car traveled $40\ km, 45\ km, 50\ km, 35\ km$ and $55\ km$. In the next five hours, it traveled with an average speed of $50\ km\ per\ hour$. Find the total distance the car traveled in 10 hours.

13) In the following figure, ABCD is a rectangle. If $a = \sqrt{3}$, and $b = 2a$, find the area of the shaded region. (the shaded region is a trapezoid)

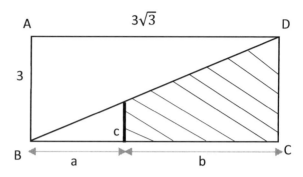

14) 6 liters of water are poured into an aquarium that's $15cm$ long, $5cm$ wide, and $90cm$ high. How many centimeters will the water level in the aquarium rise due to this added water? (1 $liter$ of $water = 1,000$ cm^3)

15) If a box contains red and blue balls in ratio of $2:3$, how many red balls are there if 90 blue balls are in the box?

16) A chemical solution contains 4% alcohol. If there is $24\ ml$ of alcohol, what is the volume of the solution?

17) If $\frac{3x}{16} = \frac{x-1}{4}$, $x =$

18) Simplify $(-5 + 9i)(3 + 5i)$.

19) If θ is an acute angle and $sin\ \theta = \frac{4}{5}$ then $cos\ \theta =$

20) If 60% of x equal to 30% of 20, then what is the value of $(x + 5)^2$?

21) A boat sails 40 miles south and then 30 miles east. How far is the boat from its start point?

22) What is the value of x in the following equation? $log_4(x + 2) - log_4(x - 2) = 1$

23) A number is chosen at random from 1 to 25. Find the probability of not selecting a composite number.

24) Find AC in the following triangle. Round answers to the nearest tenth.

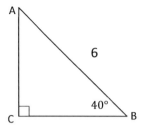

25) If $y = 4ab + 3b^3$, what is y when $a = 2$ and $b = 3$?

26) If $f(x) = 5 + x$ and $g(x) = -x^2 - 1 - 2x$, then find $(g - f)(x)$.

27) If cotangent of an angel β is 1, then the tangent of angle β is ...

28) When point $A(10,3)$ is reflected over the $y-$axis to get the point B, what are the coordinates of point B?

29) What is the average of circumference of figure A and area of figure B? $(\pi = 3)$

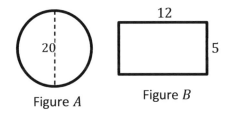

Figure A Figure B

30) If $f(x) = 2x^3 + 5x^2 + 2x$ and $g(x) = -2$, what is the value of $f(g(x))$?

This is the end of Practice Test 2.

ALEKS Mathematics Practice Tests
Answers and Explanations

Now, it's time to review your results to see where you went wrong and what areas you need to improve!

ALEKS Mathematics Practice Test 1

1) **The answer is** $\frac{4x-2}{x^2-x}$

$$\left(\frac{f}{g}\right)(x) = \frac{f(x)}{g(x)} = \frac{4x-2}{x^2-x}$$

2) **The answer is** $1,080$

Use simple interest formula: $I = prt$ (I = interest, p = principal, r = rate, t = time)

$$I = (12,000)(0.045)(2) = 1,080$$

3) **The answer is** $9,600$

Number of visiting fans: $\quad \frac{2 \times 24,000}{5} = 9,600$

4) **The answer is** $120°$

The sum of all angles in a quadrilateral is 360 degrees. Let x be the smallest angle in the quadrilateral. Then the angles are: $2x, 3x, 3x, 4x$, $2x + 3x + 3x + 4x = 360 \rightarrow 12x = 360 \rightarrow x = 30$, The angles in the quadrilateral are: $60°, 90°, 90°$, and $120°$

5) **The answer is** $\frac{7\sqrt{\pi}}{\pi}$

Formula for the area of a circle is: $A = \pi r^2$, Using 49 for the area of the circle we have: $49 = \pi r^2$, Let's solve for the radius (r). $\frac{49}{\pi} = r^2 \rightarrow r = \sqrt{\frac{49}{\pi}} = \frac{7}{\sqrt{\pi}} = \frac{7}{\sqrt{\pi}} \times \frac{\sqrt{\pi}}{\sqrt{\pi}} = \frac{7\sqrt{\pi}}{\pi}$

6) **The answer is** 90

Length of the rectangle is: $\frac{5}{4} \times 20 = 25$, perimeter of rectangle is: $2 \times (20 + 25) = 90$

7) **The answer is** $135°$

The angle x and 45 are complementary angles. Therefore: $x + 45 = 180 \rightarrow x = 180° - 45° = 135°$

8) **The answer is** 18

The sum of supplement angles is 180. Let x be that angle. Therefore, $x + 9x = 180$

$10x = 180$, divide both sides by 10: $x = 18$

9) The answer is 3

Solving Systems of Equations by Elimination: Multiply the first equation by (-2), then add it to the second equation.

$$\begin{array}{c}-2(2x + 5y = 11)\\ 4x - 2y = -14\end{array} \Rightarrow \begin{array}{c}-4x - 10y = -22\\ 4x - 2y = -14\end{array} \Rightarrow -12y = -36 \Rightarrow y = 3$$

10) The answer is $62,500$

Three times of 25,000 is 75,000. One sixth of them cancelled their tickets. One sixth of 75,000 equals $12,500$ $(\frac{1}{6} \times 72,000 = 12,500)$. $62,500$ $(72,000 - 12,000 = 62,500)$ fans are attending this week.

11) The answer is $\frac{\sqrt{8}}{3}$

$sinA = \frac{1}{3} \Rightarrow$ Since $sin\theta = \frac{opposite}{hypotenuse}$, we have the following right triangle. Then:

$c = \sqrt{3^2 - 1^2} = \sqrt{9 - 1} = \sqrt{8}, cosA = \frac{\sqrt{8}}{3}$

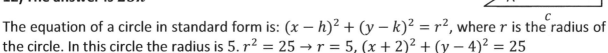

12) The answer is 25π

The equation of a circle in standard form is: $(x - h)^2 + (y - k)^2 = r^2$, where r is the radius of the circle. In this circle the radius is 5. $r^2 = 25 \rightarrow r = 5$, $(x + 2)^2 + (y - 4)^2 = 25$

Area of a circle: $A = \pi r^2 = \pi(5)^2 = 25\pi$

13) The answer is 5.8×10^5

$580,000 = 5.8 \times 10^5$

14) The answer is 200

The ratio of boy to girls is $2 : 3$. Therefore, there are 2 boys out of 5 students. To find the answer, first divide the total number of students by 5, then multiply the result by 2.

$500 \div 5 = 100 \Rightarrow 100 \times 2 = 200$

15) The answer is 40

First, find the number. Let x be the number. Write the equation and solve for x.

150% of a number is 75, then: $1.5 \times x = 75 \Rightarrow x = 75 \div 1.5 = 50$

80% of 50 is: $0.8 \times 50 = 40$

16) The answer is $\begin{bmatrix} -5 & 3 \\ 4 & -7 \end{bmatrix}$

First, find $2A$. $A = \begin{bmatrix} -1 & 2 \\ 1 & -2 \end{bmatrix}$ $\quad 2A = 2 \times \begin{bmatrix} -1 & 2 \\ 1 & -2 \end{bmatrix} = \begin{bmatrix} -2 & 4 \\ 2 & -4 \end{bmatrix}$, Now, solve for $2A - B$. $2A - B = \begin{bmatrix} -2 & 4 \\ 2 & -4 \end{bmatrix} - \begin{bmatrix} 3 & 1 \\ -2 & 3 \end{bmatrix} = \begin{bmatrix} -2-3 & 4-1 \\ 2-(-2) & -4-3 \end{bmatrix} = \begin{bmatrix} -5 & 3 \\ 4 & -7 \end{bmatrix}$

17) The answer is $x \geq 6 \cup x \leq -2$

$x - 2 \geq 4 \rightarrow x \geq 4 + 2 \rightarrow x \geq 6$, Or $x - 2 \leq -4 \rightarrow x \leq -4 + 2 \rightarrow x \leq -2$

Then, solution is: $\quad x \geq 6 \cup x \leq -2$

18) The answer is $\frac{8}{17}$

$\tan = \frac{opposite}{adjacent}$, and $\tan x = \frac{8}{15}$, therefore, the opposite side of the angle x is 8 and the adjacent side is 15. Let's draw the triangle.

Using Pythagorean theorem, we have:

$a^2 + b^2 = c^2 \rightarrow 8^2 + 15^2 = c^2 \rightarrow 64 + 225 = c^2 \rightarrow c = 17$, $\sin x = \frac{opposite}{hypotenuse} = \frac{8}{17}$

19) The answer is $x^{\frac{21}{4}}$

$(x^6)^{\frac{7}{8}} = x^{6 \times \frac{7}{8}} = x^{\frac{42}{8}} = x^{\frac{21}{4}}$

20) The answer are $0, -2, -3$

Frist factor the function: $f(x) = x^3 + 5x^2 + 6x = x(x+2)(x+3)$, To find the zeros, $f(x)$ should be zero. $f(x) = x(x+2)(x+3) = 0$, Therefore, the zeros are: $x = 0$, $\quad (x+2) = 0 \Rightarrow x = -2$,

$(x+3) = 0 \Rightarrow x = -3$

21) The answer is 2

$\sin^2 a + \cos^2 a = 1$, then: $x + 1 = 3$, $\quad\quad x = 2$

22) The answer is $\frac{y}{5}$

Solve for x. $\sqrt{5x} = \sqrt{y}$. $\quad$ Square both sides of the equation: $(\sqrt{5x})^2 = (\sqrt{y})^2 \quad\quad 5x = y$

$\quad x = \frac{y}{5}$

23) The answer is 59.48

$average = \frac{sum\ of\ terms}{number\ of\ terms}$, The sum of the weight of all girls is: $18 \times 55 = 990\ kg$

The sum of the weight of all boys is: $32 \times 62 = 1,984\ kg$, The sum of the weight of all students is: $990 + 1,984 = 2,974\ kg$. $average = \frac{2,974}{50} = 59.48$

24) The answer is 46

Plug in the value of x and y. $x = 3$ and $y = -3$

$$5(x - 2y) + (2 - x)^2 = 5(3 - 2(-3)) + (2 - 3)^2 = 5(3 + 6) + (-1)^2 = 45 + 1 = 46$$

25) The answer is 16%

The question is this: 530.40 is what percent of 631? Use percent formula: $part = \frac{percent}{100} \times whole$. $530.40 = \frac{percent}{100} \times 631 \Rightarrow 530.40 = \frac{percent \times 631}{100} \Rightarrow 53,040 = percent \times 631 \Rightarrow percent = \frac{53,040}{631} = 84$. 530.40 is 84% of 631. Therefore, the discount is: $100\% - 84\% = 16\%$

26) The answer is $\frac{1}{2}$

The relationship among all sides of right triangle $30° - 60° - 90°$ is provided in the following triangle: Sine of $30°$ equals to: $\frac{opposite}{hypotenus} = \frac{x}{2x} = \frac{1}{2}$

27) The answer is $\frac{3}{4} + i$

To simplify the fraction, multiply both numerator and denominator by i.

$\frac{4-3i}{-4i} \times \frac{i}{i} = \frac{4i-3i^2}{-4i^2}, i^2 - 1$, Then: $\frac{4i-3i^2}{-4i^2} = \frac{4i-3(-1)}{-4(-1)} = \frac{4i+3}{4} = \frac{4i}{4} + \frac{3}{4} = \frac{3}{4} + i$

28) The answer is 38

Let x be the smallest number. Then, these are the numbers: $x, x + 1, x + 2, x + 3, x + 4$

$$average = \frac{sum\ of\ terms}{number\ of\ terms} \Rightarrow 40 = \frac{x+(x+1)+(x+2)+(x+3)+(x+4)}{5} \Rightarrow 40 = \frac{5x+10}{5} \Rightarrow$$

$$200 = 5x + 10 \Rightarrow 190 = 5x \Rightarrow x = 38$$

29) The answer is $-\frac{1}{2}$

The equation of a line in slope intercept form is: $y = mx + b$, Solve for y. $4x - 2y = 14 \Rightarrow -2y = 14 - 4x \Rightarrow y = (14 - 4x) \div (-2) \Rightarrow y = 2x - 7$, The slope is 2. The slope of the line perpendicular to this line is: $m_1 \times m_2 = -1 \Rightarrow 2 \times m_2 = -1 \Rightarrow m_2 = -\frac{1}{2}$

30) The answer is $\frac{2}{x^3} + 4$

$$f\big(g(x)\big) = 2 \times (\frac{1}{x})^3 + 4 = \frac{2}{x^3} + 4$$

ALEKS Mathematics Practice Test 2

1) The answer is 18

The area of the floor is: $6\ cm\ \times\ 24\ cm = 144\ cm^2$. The number is tiles needed $= 144 \div 8 = 18$

2) The answer is 32

The diagonal of the square is 8. Let x be the side.

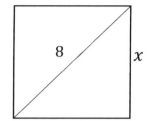

Use Pythagorean Theorem: $a^2 + b^2 = c^2$

$x^2 + x^2 = 8^2 \Rightarrow 2x^2 = 8^2 \Rightarrow\ 2x^2 = 64 \Rightarrow x^2 = 32 \Rightarrow x = \sqrt{32}$

The area of the square is: $\sqrt{32} \times \sqrt{32} = 32$

3) The answer is 145

$x = 20 + 125 = 145$

4) The answer is 5

Solve the system of equations by elimination method.

$\begin{array}{l} 3x - 4y = -20 \\ \underline{-x + 2y = 10} \end{array}$ Multiply the second equation by 3, then add it to the first equation.

$\begin{array}{l} 3x - 4y = -20 \\ \underline{3(-x + 2y = 10)} \end{array} \Rightarrow \begin{array}{l} 3x - 4y = -20 \\ \underline{-3x + 6y = 30)} \end{array} \Rightarrow$ add the equations $2y = 10 \Rightarrow y = 5$

5) The answer is 8.4 hours

Use distance formula: $Distance = Rate \times time \Rightarrow 420 = 50 \times T$, divide both sides by

50. $420 \div 50 = T \Rightarrow T = 8.4\ hours$. Change hours to minutes for the decimal part. $0.4\ hours = 0.4 \times 60 = 24\ minutes$.

6) The answer is 96

40% of 60 equals to: $0.40 \times 60 = 24$, 12% of 600 equals to: $0.12 \times 600 = 72$

40% of 60 is added to 12% of 600: $24 + 72 = 96$

7) The answer is $7 \leq x \leq 13$
$|x - 10| \leq 3 \rightarrow -3 \leq x - 10 \leq 3 \rightarrow -3 + 10 \leq x - 10 + 10 \leq 3 + 10 \rightarrow 7 \leq x \leq 13$

8) The answer is 40

The area of ΔBED is 16, then: $\frac{4 \times AB}{2} = 16 \rightarrow 4 \times AB = 32 \rightarrow AB = 8$

The area of ΔBDF is 18, then: $\frac{3 \times BC}{2} = 18 \rightarrow 3 \times BC = 36 \rightarrow BC = 12$

The perimeter of the rectangle is $= 2 \times (8 + 12) = 40$

9) The answer is $36\,ft$

Write a proportion and solve for x. $\frac{3}{2} = \frac{x}{24} \Rightarrow 2x = 3 \times 24 \Rightarrow x = 36\,ft$

10) The answer is $60\,ft$

The relationship among all sides of special right triangle

$30° - 60° - 90°$ is provided in this triangle:

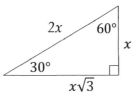

In this triangle, the opposite side of $30°$ angle is half of the hypotenuse.

Draw the shape of this question:

The latter is the hypotenuse. Therefore, the latter is $60\,ft$.

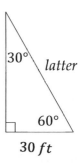

11) The answer is $y^5 + 2x^3 + 7z^3 + x^2 - 2y^2$

$2x^2 + 3y^5 - x^2 + 2z^3 - 2y^2 + 2x^3 - 2y^5 + 5z^3$
$\quad = 2x^2 - x^2 + 2x^3 - 2y^2 + 3y^5 - 2y^5 + 2z^3 + 5z^3$
$\quad = x^2 + 2x^3 - 2y^2 + y^5 + 7z^3$

Write the expression in standard form:

$x^2 + 2x^3 - 2y^2 + y^5 + 7z^3 = y^5 + 2x^3 + 7z^3 + x^2 - 2y^2$

12) The answer is 475

Add the first 5 numbers. $40 + 45 + 50 + 35 + 55 = 225$

To find the distance traveled in the next 5 hours, multiply the average by number of hours.

$Distance = Average \times Rate = 50 \times 5 = 250.$ Add both numbers. $250 + 225 = 475$

13) The answer is $4\sqrt{3}$

Based on triangle similarity theorem: $\frac{a}{a+b} = \frac{c}{3} \rightarrow c = \frac{3a}{a+b} = \frac{3\sqrt{3}}{3\sqrt{3}} = 1 \rightarrow$ area of shaded region is:

$\left(\frac{c+3}{2}\right)(b) = \frac{4}{2} \times 2\sqrt{3} = 4\sqrt{3}$

14) The answer is $80cm$

$One\ liter = 1,000\ cm^3 \rightarrow 6\ liters = 6,000\ cm^3$ $6,000 = 15 \times 5 \times h \rightarrow h = \frac{6,000}{75} = 80cm$

15) The answer is 60

$$\frac{2}{3} \times 90 = 60$$

16) The answer is $600 \ ml$

4% of the volume of the solution is alcohol. Let x be the volume of the solution.

Then: $4\% \ of \ x = 24 \ ml \Rightarrow 0.04 \ x = 24 \Rightarrow x = 24 \div 0.04 = 600$

17) The answer is 4

Solve for x. $\frac{3x}{16} = \frac{x-1}{4}$. Multiply the second fraction by 4. $\frac{3x}{16} = \frac{4(x-1)}{4 \times 4}$. Tow denominators are equal. Therefore, the numerators must be equal. $3x = 4x - 4, \quad 0 = x - 4, 4 = x$

18) The answer is $-60 + 2i$

We know that: $i = \sqrt{-1} \Rightarrow i^2 = -1$

$(-5 + 9i)(3 + 5i) = -15 - 25i + 27i + 45i^2 = -15 + 2i - 45 = -60 + 2i$

19) The answer is $\frac{3}{5}$

$sin\theta = \frac{4}{5} \Rightarrow$ we have following triangle, then

$c = \sqrt{5^2 - 4^2} = \sqrt{25 - 16} = \sqrt{9} = 3, cos\theta = \frac{3}{5}$

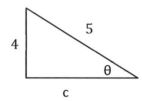

20) The answer is 225

$0.6x = (0.3) \times 20 \rightarrow x = 10 \rightarrow (x + 5)^2 = (15)^2 = 225$

21) The answer is $50 \ miles$

Use the information provided in the question to draw the shape.

Use Pythagorean Theorem: $a^2 + b^2 = c^2$

$40^2 + 30^2 = c^2 \Rightarrow 1,600 + 900 = c^2 \Rightarrow 2,500 = c^2 \Rightarrow c = 50$

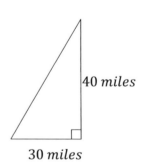

40 miles

30 miles

22) The answer is $\frac{10}{3}$

<u>METHOD ONE</u>

$log_4(x + 2) - log_4(x - 2) = 1$, Add $log_4(x - 2)$ to both sides

$log_4(x + 2) - log_4(x - 2) + log_4(x - 2) = 1 + log_4(x - 2)$

$log_4(x + 2) = 1 + log_4(x - 2)$

Apply logarithm rule: $a = log_b(b^a) \Rightarrow 1 = log_4(4^1) = log_4(4)$

then: $log_4(x + 2) = log_4(4) + log_4(x - 2)$

Logarithm rule: $log_c(a) + log_c(b) = log_c(ab)$

then: $log_4(4) + log_4(x - 2) = log_4(4(x - 2))$

$\log_4(x + 2) = \log_4(4(x - 2))$

When the logs have the same base: $log_b(f(x)) = log_b(g(x)) = f(x) = g(x)$

$(x + 2) = 4(x - 2), x = \dfrac{10}{3}$

METHOD TWO

We know that: $\qquad log_a b - log_a c = log_a \dfrac{b}{c}$ and $\qquad log_a b = c \Rightarrow b = a^c$

Then: $log_4(x + 2) - log_4(x - 2) = log_4 \dfrac{x+2}{x-2} = 1 \Rightarrow \dfrac{x+2}{x-2} = 4^1 = 4 \Rightarrow x + 2 = 4(x - 2)$

$\Rightarrow x + 2 = 4x - 8 \Rightarrow 4x - x = 8 + 2 \rightarrow 3x = 10 \Rightarrow x = \dfrac{10}{3}$

23) The answer is $\dfrac{2}{5}$

Set of number that are not composite between 1 and 25: $A = \{1, 2, 3, 5, 7, 11, 13, 17, 19, 23\}$

$Probability = \dfrac{number\ of\ desired\ outcomes}{number\ of\ total\ outcomes} = \dfrac{10}{25} = \dfrac{2}{5}$

24) The answer is 3.9

$sine\ \theta = \dfrac{opposite}{hypotenuse}. \ sine\ 40° = \dfrac{AC}{6} \rightarrow 6 \times sine\ 40° = AC,$

now use a calculator to find $sine\ 40°$. $sine\ 40° \cong 0.642 \rightarrow AC \cong 3.9$

25) The answer is 105

$y = 4ab + 3b^3$. Plug in the values of a and b in the equation: $a = 2$ and $b = 3$

$y = 4(2)(3) + 3(3)^3 = 24 + 3(27) = 24 + 81 = 105$

26) The answer is $-x^2 - 3x - 6$

$(g - f)(x) = g(x) - f(x) = (-x^2 - 1 - 2x) - (5 + x)$

$-x^2 - 1 - 2x - 5 - x = -x^2 - 3x - 6$

27) The answer is 1

$tangent\ \beta = \dfrac{1}{cotangent\ \beta} = \dfrac{1}{1} = 1$

28) The answer is $(-10, 3)$

When points are reflected over y-axis, the value of y in the coordinates doesn't change and the sign of x changes. Therefore, the coordinates of point B is $(-10, 3)$.

29) The answer is 60

Perimeter of figure A is: $2\pi r = 2\pi\frac{20}{2} = 20\pi = 20 \times 3 = 60$

Area of figure B is: $5 \times 12 = 60$, $Average = \frac{60+6}{2} = \frac{120}{2} = 60$

30) The answer is 0

$g(x) = -2$, then $f(g(x)) = f(-2) = 2\,(-2)^3 + 5(-2)^2 + 2(-2) = -16 + 20 - 4 = 0$

"Effortless Math" Publications

Effortless Math authors' team strives to prepare and publish the best quality Mathematics learning resources to make learning Math easier for all. We hope that our publications help you or your student Math in an effective way.

We all in Effortless Math wish you good luck and successful studies!

Effortless Math Authors

www.EffortlessMath.com

... So Much More Online!

✓ FREE Math lessons

✓ More Math learning books!

✓ Mathematics Worksheets

✓ Online Math Tutors

Need a PDF version of this book?

Visit www.EffortlessMath.com

Receive the PDF version of this book or get another FREE book!

Thank you for using our Book!

Do you LOVE this book?

Then, you can get the PDF version of this book or another book absolutely FREE!

Please email us at:

info@EffortlessMath.com

for details.

Made in the USA
San Bernardino, CA
10 March 2020